C000177802

Connecting
with
Cancer

Published by

**MELROSE
BOOKS**

An Imprint of Melrose Press Limited
St Thomas Place, Ely
Cambridgeshire
CB7 4GG, UK
www.melrosebooks.co.uk

FIRST EDITION

Copyright © Cancer Connections Ltd 2017

The editor, illustrator and contributors assert their moral rights to
be identified as the owners of this work

Cover designed by Robert Olley and Melrose Books

**ISBN   978-1-912026-35-7 (paperback)
        978-1-912026-38-8 (printed paper case)
epub   978-1-912026-36-4
mobi   978-1-912026-37-1**

All rights reserved. No part of this publication may be reproduced, stored in a retrieval system, or transmitted, in any form or by
any means electronic, mechanical, photocopying, recording or otherwise, without the prior permission of the publishers.

This book is sold subject to the condition that it shall not, by way of trade or otherwise, be lent, re-sold, hired out or otherwise
circulated without the publisher's prior consent in any form of binding or cover other than that in which it is published and without
a similar condition including this condition being imposed on the subsequent purchaser.

Printed and bound in Great Britain by:
Ashford Colour Press Ltd
Unit 600
Fareham Reach
Fareham Road
Gosport
PO13 0FW

Connecting
with
Cancer

Living with and beyond cancer

R R Hall
with illustrations by Robert Olley

Contents

Introduction

HEARING THE DOCTOR SAY, 'I'm sorry, it's not good news: it's cancer' is almost always devastating and for those who hear it life is seldom the same again. Although many improvements in the treatment of cancer have been achieved, and the causes of some cancers are better understood, the 'Big C' can still seem a formidable and lonely mountain to climb. Very often a cancer diagnosis means dealing with uncertainty, anger, fear, grief, loss of control, faltering self-confidence – so many emotions and practical problems that people who have not had cancer never understand.

What is it like to discover you have a possibly fatal disease? What does it feel like to go home from hospital to tell the family? What happens if I need major surgery, weeks of radiotherapy and months of chemotherapy and am unable to work for months on end? How will I manage if I lose my job and struggle financially – all because of cancer? Do the doctors realise how many sleepless nights I spend waiting for the result of the biopsy? Does anyone care how hard it is to share my fear with people whom I love most? What should we do when our child is in trouble at school because they think I'm dying? How can I help my loved ones to cope if I am no longer here? Questions such as these are discussed only rarely in the surgeon's office or the oncology clinic.

As a surgeon, my job had been to remove cancer as skilfully as possible and then make sure, with the help of nurses and other medical staff, that its owner made a safe and speedy recovery. I saw them afterwards to oversee and encourage their progress, but what happened in their personal life, how they coped with the consequences of their cancer, in their family, at work and in their social life, was not usually my main concern; nor was it the focus for most of my colleagues.

When asked what they would appreciate most, a group of people who had experienced cancer replied, "Someone to talk to who understands." Or, as one man explained, "When I heard I had cancer, I needed to talk to somebody. Not a busy doctor with only minutes to spare. Not a nurse who could have no idea what it is like to be a man who has just been told he has cancer. I needed to talk with someone who had experienced what all this would mean to me and my family. To me, as a member of the human race, there is an inherent need to communicate, to express my feelings and fears."

Bearing this in mind, and remembering a chance encounter with a distressed stranger in a bookshop, and the example shown by the professor of surgery late one night when I was a newly qualified doctor, I discussed these questions with friends. The outcome was an experiment: we started a local cancer support charity run by volunteers who did understand what cancer was like and who could answer the questions because they had experienced cancer themselves. We called it Cancer Connections. Over the past ten years, more than four thousand people affected by cancer have walked through the door and been encouraged to talk. As our volunteers have listened we have learned how different the cancer experience can be. Also, that there are common threads and by sharing their experiences visitors have learned that they are not alone and have been helped to move on. Talking and sharing has been therapeutic. The purpose of this book, therefore, is to share these experiences with an even wider audience in the hope that others may benefit too.

Seeking help from a cancer support group is by no means the only way to 'cope' with cancer. Many, many people do so on their own or find the support they need from family, close friends, colleagues, their GP or hospital staff. Thus, to achieve our objective, thirty-four contributors from varying backgrounds and different walks of life, some from Cancer Connections and some from elsewhere, have recorded their experience of cancer and the recordings have then been transcribed for publication. Two other contributors have written their own personal account; seventeen different types of cancer have been included.

Here, in the pages that follow, there is not an on-going single narrative nor any 'professional' commentary or analysis, just snippets of conversation, anecdotes and personal stories as told by each individual contributor about her or his experience of cancer. In this way we hope you will discover at first-hand what cancer feels like. If you wish you can also learn how it is possible to manage the upheaval that follows a cancer diagnosis, how others have overcome the problems that it causes, and how they have been enabled to make the most of life after cancer.

As a reader you may wish to start, not at the beginning, but with a particular type of cancer or an aspect of the cancer experience that concerns you most. To help you do so, we have included an index which you will find on page 167.

Thank you

Connecting with Cancer has been possible only with the help of the contributors who have been willing to share their very personal experience. To hear these stories has often been moving, sometimes distressing and, on occasions, troubling. But it has also been educational, remarkable, heart-warming and always uplifting. Helping to write them has been a privilege.

My very special thanks to:

Annabel – Ashley Bruce – Annie Campion – Lynne Croft – Jackie Dixon
Audrey Donnelly – Elizabeth – Patricia Fawcett – Diane Ferguson
Michelle Grimmer – Derek Gouldsbra – Joyce Groombridge
Rachel Groombridge – Lee Hall – Linda Hind – Amy Horton – Jason Kaid
Paul Kan – Louise – Noreen McKiernan – Jane Maher – George Oxberry
Bob Olley – John Pattison – Sheila Rooney – Tony Sherwin – Debra Slesser
Philip Smith – Stan Stallard – Anne Stutchbury – Sarah Ward – Roy Wilburn
Paul Wilson – Jackie Younger – Roger Younger
Eliza, Emily & Olivia

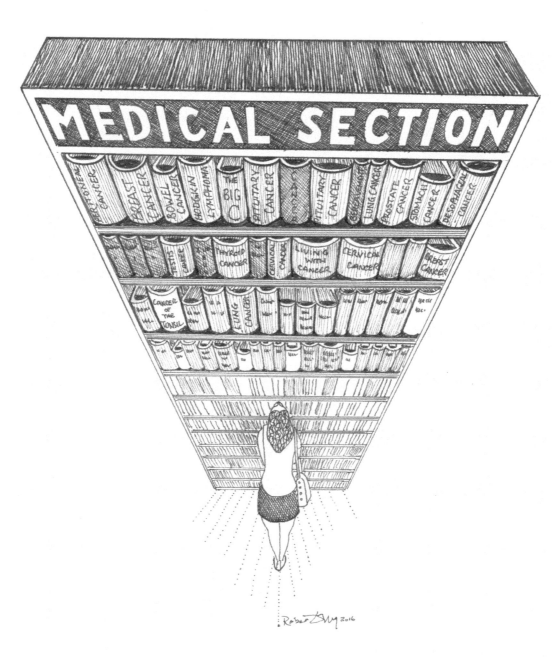

The bookshop

IT WAS IN THE DAYS BEFORE on-line shopping and next day delivery, so a trip to the bookshop was needed. Searching the shelves in a rather gloomy corner of the medical section, I became aware that there was a woman standing a few feet away, crying. I had encountered a few unusual situations in life before, but this was a new one. She was middle aged, a total stranger, appeared to be alone and was clearly distressed, weeping uncontrollably. Concentrating on finding my own book I tried to ignore her, but it was no good; there were no shop assistants in sight, no other customers. I would have to do something.

"Excuse me. I do not wish to intrude, but there seems to be a problem. Can I help in any way?" She looked startled but fished a tissue from her bag and dried her eyes.

"I'm looking for something about cancer," she replied. "I've just come from the hospital. The doctor told me I've got breast cancer. I can't believe it, I never dreamed the lump would be that. Apparently I'll have to have an operation and maybe some other treatment – God knows what, I've no idea. I don't understand. Am I going to die? They probably told me some more, but I didn't hear a word after that one. I need to know what's going to happen to me – so I came here.

"Where else could I go?"

It's not good news

SURGEON: "YOU'VE GOT CANCER but we can keep you going for a few months or maybe a few years."

Me: "Okay, which is it: months or years?"

Surgeon: No answer.

Me: "Will it kill me?"

Surgeon: "Yes, it probably will."

That was when my head went into overdrive and I lost the plot. I was angry with myself for not going to the doctor earlier and I was angry with the way my wife and I had been told the diagnosis. We needed to get some order back into life, work out what was important and what was not.

YOU NEVER FORGET the day they tell you. The surgeon was not a man to beat about the bush: "I've got to tell you you've got stomach cancer." Right. Well. You go numb. Nothing. Everything. The world seemed to stop. It was surreal.

WHEN THE CAMERA up my backside revealed all, the fellow who was doing it said he'd found something and he was ninety percent sure it was cancer. Thanks, just what I wanted to know!

THE SURGEON WAS EXPLAINING things, drawing diagrams, saying what they could do, telling me it was good because it was unusual to diagnose it early like me – but he had just told me I had cancer! It's that word, it's still frightening.

SITTING IN THE CLINIC and hearing that it was cancer, my husband couldn't speak and was more upset than me. Going home was a blur. When we got there we sat on the sofa looking at the garden and cried, and cried. The phone kept ringing, but we didn't answer; we couldn't face speaking to anybody.

MY OVERRIDING THOUGHT was not to worry about the prognosis, or being frightened that I might die, but to remember the upheaval we had when my brother died. I needed to get organised. When I was asked how I felt, all I could say was that we would need to get the house cleared!

WHEN WE WERE FIRST TOLD it was terminal, we went for a walk by the hospital and my husband said, "I'm sorry you have backed a loser. I'm sorry I've let you down." I didn't feel that way at all and told him so; we both knew there was not going to be a happy ending, but we needed to be able to hope. That worked for us and kept us together.

WHEN THE CONSULTANT LOOKED a bit solemn and said, "Oh, are you on your own?" I went 'Oh, Oh!' and knew something was up. I asked him if it was cancer and he said 'Yes'. Apparently it was a rather rare cancer and they had found lots of nodules in lots of places. They showed me all the scans and pictures of the tumours taken at the laparoscopy, and I found that very helpful. The worst bit is knowing that you've got to tell the family.

THE BIOPSY was on the Friday and I had to go for the results the following Tuesday, but I went straight into work and cleared my desk: I knew I wouldn't be back for a while. Although I was expecting it, when the surgeon said it was cancer it was still a shock. I had a five-year-old daughter at school and my first question was, "Am I going to die?"

Fortunately the nurse replied, "Yes you are, but we can't tell you when or what of."

It was a strange thing to say and I didn't take it in at the time, but it was reassuring and has stayed with me for the past twelve years.

AFTER THE MAMMOGRAM and the needle I left the clinic and went back to work, but within a couple of hours I was back for the result. It was cancer. A few minutes later I was driving out of the hospital car park. When I had driven round the roundabout three times, it dawned on me that I could not remember the way home. My only thoughts were 'Get yourself pulled together. What are you going to tell your six children?'

I WENT TO THE CLINIC on my own, not expecting serious news. The mole was not just a mole, it was 'malignant' and I didn't quite know what 'malignant' meant. The dermatologist said that I should have an operation to remove more skin and go further to remove the 'cells' or it would spread. Now, when someone says it could 'spread' the alarm bells started ringing.

THE CONSULTANT'S OPINION was definite. "I am afraid you have prostate cancer. It has broken out of the organ. It is an aggressive cancer with a high Gleason score." Just the comments I was dreading to hear. I had done a bit of research on the internet and my prognosis, I felt, was not good.

"How do you feel?"
How do I feel? What a question!
Numb? Devastated? The bombshell had dropped!

I WAS IN THE OFFICE when the surgeon telephoned. When he said nothing but that he wanted to see me I guessed, and could not stay in the office. I went outside and bawled my eyes out. When I reached home, I went for a walk in the park with my wife. We sat by the pond and cuddled, and told each other we'd face it together although we really had no idea what lay ahead. Later, when we saw the surgeon and he confirmed it was cancer, it rocked me to the core. Everything rushed through my mind like a sort of madness. It was crazy and for weeks I lived in a big blur; it felt surreal because things were happening around me, but I didn't feel I was there. Fortunately, these feelings changed: I got the 'Let's beat this thing!' mindset and things picked up.

I WAS FASCINATED when they looked inside because on the video screen it looked just like a mouldy cauliflower with bits floating around; I was very interested in what I saw, but not really worried. I understood what was being said, I understood what I was being shown and I understood what might happen, but it failed to penetrate to cause me any fear. I did not feel emotional about it and decided that, well, this is where I am; it wasn't that I didn't care what might happen, but felt that whatever that might be I would do the best I could. I waited to hear it but 'cancer' was never actually mentioned. The consultant agreed that the cauliflower we had seen on the screen was 'it' and the bits floating round were 'debris'. The nurse was busy elsewhere and I could not wait indefinitely to see her and the young doctor was too flummoxed to say 'yes' when I asked him if I had cancer. However, I knew, and my immediate thoughts were to sort out my own needs.

IT WAS THE Head and Neck surgeon who told me. It was cancer of my voice box, the larynx. I realised I would need an operation, but I never thought I would end up with a hole in my neck. The consultant gave me a pamphlet and a CD to look at so that I could see what would be involved. When I looked at the information at home, my reaction was to go into overdrive mode. I had a phobia of hospitals, it looked a big operation and although I couldn't tell exactly what would happen, it said I would not be able to talk again. I decided this was not going to happen to me.

WHEN THE X-RAY SHOWED A SHADOW, I went straight to my GP who I've known for years: I was shattered, but I needed to know. She said, "Best case scenario, you'll have a few treatments and it will be gone, worst case it's recurrent melanoma and that's it." She knew what I was like, she was there when my sister passed away; she knew I would want the truth. When it was confirmed melanoma she telephoned me to say that it might not be so bad because there were some new treatments available and I would see an oncologist. However, I was given a DS 1500 form for a welfare benefits application so I knew my expected prognosis could be less than six months. The doctors might slow it down, but they couldn't cure it. I was forty-three with a wife, two children, three grandchildren and an early army pension.

IT'S A LONG TIME AGO and I was seventeen at the time. I was told nothing. Later I learned that my parents were told I probably had a malignancy. My mum told my best friend, "They think John's got cancer, but we don't want him to know," and after that, all my friends stopped coming to see me. Sent to the radiotherapy ward, I was greeted by a doctor who said, "This is the young man with Hodgkin lymphoma," but that meant nothing to me. However, when I bought a paper to pass the hospital hours away I saw the headline 'Crossroads star hides secret from millions of fans'. Reading further, it explained that the star had Hodgkin lymphoma, a lymphatic cancer. That was what I had, wasn't it? That's how I discovered I had cancer. I asked one of the nurses but she would not tell me and it was only when I confronted my mum that I was told the truth: there was only a fifty-fifty chance of cure.

WE KNEW THE NEWS was not good when we saw the Macmillan nurse sitting with the consultant when we went in; he said it was inoperable, but we didn't take it in. Joyce had lung cancer and really didn't want to know. I will always remember because the letter from the hospital was written professional to professional, stating the facts: very harsh, and we hadn't asked for a copy as far as I can remember. It said that Joyce had a terminal illness, that treatment would not be beneficial and they would provide just palliative care. Joyce read the letter, threw it down and burst into tears. When it's in black and white you can't escape the reality. That is my one regret: if I could have stopped the letter from the hospital, I would.

WHEN I RECEIVED THE RECALL LETTER two days after the mammogram, I knew it was cancer, because when I prayed, God did not tell me that everything would be all right. Instead, when I read the Bible I found this: 'Do not fear for I am with you. Do not be dismayed, I am your God. I will strengthen you and help you'. I wrote that on a small piece of paper and kept it in my hand when I went to the hospital – and I carry it with me now.

WHEN I HEARD that I had breast cancer the second time, I was pretty pole-axed and couldn't help feeling it was someone else's turn. It was fifteen years after the first cancer that I found a lump in the other breast. It was cancer, again. The thought of doing the radiotherapy and chemo again was not so scary, because I knew what it would involve: it would be pretty grim, but I would just get on and deal with it. I had got through it before and I would do the same again.

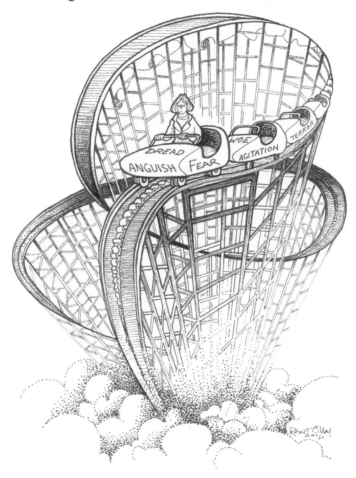

Is it a *real* cancer?

Sheila had worked as a nurse for many years, but could not believe that the tumour in her breast was a real cancer: that was not supposed to happen to her.

WHEN I GOT THE LETTER asking me to go back after the mammogram, I thought they had just lost the x-ray. But they hadn't. I had the scan and the biopsy and a cup of coffee. Two hours later the doctor confirmed it was cancer. Well, you really could have knocked me over with a feather; I'm still embarrassed about it. When I saw the surgeon at the next appointment, I said to him, "Can I ask you something? Is it a *real* cancer?" The previous mammograms had all been normal and I had no expectation for this one to be any different; it was going to be totally normal. There was a reason why

I was so sure. I had cared for my sister-in-law when she had breast cancer and she had a particularly difficult time. I also had a close friend who had breast cancer at the same time, and she died within a few weeks of my sister-in-law. It was all too much for me to think about. I was absolutely determined that I would never get breast cancer, ever. There was no way that could happen to me! Looking back, I can see that I was so sure because I was terrified. I was a nurse, but I could not get my head round the idea that I had cancer. I said to the friend who was with me, "This won't change my life, it's not a proper cancer, it won't be a problem." That was the state of mind I created for myself which was a shame, because things did not go according to my plan.

A CT scan and more biopsies found that the cancer was in a lymph node and there was cancer somewhere else in the breast as well. Although they were very nice about it and explained everything, I began to wonder if there might be even more cancer that had been missed. I wanted a mastectomy. Before breast cancer, I had worked as a nurse in the north-east of England, London, Switzerland, Australia and New Zealand including ten years in oncology, but that had been many years before; by the time I was diagnosed, my oncology knowledge was fifteen years out of date.

When I said I wanted a mastectomy, not a lumpectomy, I had the feeling that I was being a nuisance. As a result, I became confused and that was the start of my psychological distress. I thought I knew how to cope with cancer, but I didn't. As a healthcare professional, you think you know what it's going to be like, but when it actually happens to you it's very different! I was feeling really fit and was planning to go back to work, but that would have to wait. I remember very little of the first few weeks back at home except that housework did not get done and I thought my house would never be clean again. It did get clean, eventually, but in the meantime, life was about other priorities.

After surgery, chemotherapy would be next. However, by the time the chemotherapy was due to start I was angry, blazingly angry! I wasn't supposed to have chemotherapy because it wasn't a real cancer. This wasn't supposed to be happening to me and I was not sure I would have any. Fortunately, by the end, with the help of a skilled counsellor, my anger was beaten into submission and I completed the recommended treatment.

I trusted NHS colleagues who would know what I needed, but I found that things had changed since I retired. Nowadays, it seems, everything is organised according to 'pathways'. You start on a pathway and continue on the pathway, but if your care needs don't fit that pathway, you don't get that care.

Some people use the word 'journey' to describe what happens – they call it 'the patient journey', but I hate that: setting off on a journey suggests that you have some choice about where you go but, with cancer, there is no choice. You are a very reluctant traveller, the hotels are awful, the food is dreadful and you're travel sick!

Mastectomy

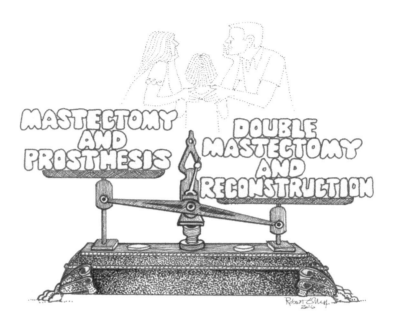

I
T HAD TO BE A MASTECTOMY; I didn't have any choice. The good news was that the hospital was doing breast reconstruction surgery and I was able to have the mastectomy, reconstruction and a reduction on the other side to balance things up, all at the same time. The other good part was that I had been very big since early teen age and had even asked to have breast reduction surgery when I was only fourteen which, of course, was refused. I didn't like my breasts and was very self-conscious, so for me, actually having breast cancer was a blessing because I was able to get rid of what I had to put up with for all those years.

WHAT DID BOTHER ME was the scar. Although I was a nurse, I had never seen anyone who had had a mastectomy and I needed to know what I would look like afterwards; I wanted to see photographs so that I could prepare myself. I made a special appointment to see the Breast Nurse. She was very kind and showed me the flip-chart pictures she had. They showed a small scar about five or six inches long, much better than I had expected.

I was quite surprised, but if that was how it would be there was no reason to worry. The reality, of course, was something different. When the dressings came off, I had such a shock. The incision went right round the side because a thorough lymph node removal had been necessary. Nobody had warned me about that.

A LOT OF PEOPLE THINK having the other breast off was drastic, but I am so glad that I did it. Going back every year for a mammogram would be a constant reminder. I was told it was only a one percent risk of getting cancer in the other breast, but I didn't want even that. Mastectomy took away that anxiety. I knew it could come back somewhere else, but this was something I could do. For me, psychologically, it was the right decision. It was not just for me, either. I did not want the worry for my little girl.

WHEN WE FOUND that I had the faulty breast cancer gene, it was suggested that I should have a second mastectomy with immediate double reconstruction. By this time, I was fed up with shopping for clothes wearing a prosthesis: it's horrible and I had already wondered about reconstruction. We talked about it, my husband was for it, and with the high chance of the cancer coming back there really wasn't any choice: another mastectomy and reconstruction it would have to be. If there hadn't been the offer of reconstruction though, it would not have been such an easy decision. I really do not know what I would have done. When you lose one boob you can match up, but if there is nothing at all, it takes away the feeling of being a woman. Fortunately, I didn't have to think about that.

Thumbs up

THE ARTIST WAS WORKING on a painting in the studio at the back of his gallery in the centre of town. His latest work hung on the walls of the gallery and, as always, the door was open to passing customers. The morning had been quiet so he had been able to work undisturbed, but nearing lunchtime, a youngish lady walked in. Looking up from his easel, he greeted her with a cheery 'Good morning', but she did not reply. Instead, saying nothing, she took her own tour of the gallery looking at each work of art. Having seen all there was to be seen she started again, standing a long time before each picture. "I could see that she was looking at the paintings but she was not taking them in; her mind was somewhere else. For some reason, I could sense that there was something not quite right, so I asked her if she was all right."

As she turned round, he could see her eyes were full of tears. Slowly she explained that she had had a mastectomy for breast cancer, but her husband could not accept it and they were having problems. "I had no idea what to say. She was a total stranger. I knew almost nothing about breast cancer and even less about mastectomy, so I said nothing. There was nothing I could say to help her. However, I must have looked sympathetic because she accepted my offer of a cup of coffee, settled down and stayed for nearly an hour, and I just listened as she talked.

"It was a year later and I called in to one of the pubs along the road for a pint. There was a snug at the front with a bar and then the main room beyond. Standing at the bar, I saw a lady in the room with her husband, who had his back to me, talking and drinking with their friends. I recognised her immediately: she was my surprise visitor from the year before. I had wondered sometimes how she had fared; had her problem been solved, had her cancer been cured? I realised there was no reason to think I would ever know. Now, here she was. She recognised me, too, and she caught my gaze. Smiling, and with what must have been a quizzical face, I raised a tentative thumb above my glass. With an even bigger smile and confidence in her eyes she looked straight back, raised her thumb in reply, and said silently, 'Thank you.'"

Sometimes it's in the genes

THE PROFESSOR WE SAW explained that finding a faulty gene was like looking for a spelling mistake in a book in the British Library whose author and title you didn't know! That was eighteen years ago and they know a lot more about genetics now.

I have four sisters. My older sister was diagnosed with breast cancer when she was forty-five and because our mum's mother had breast cancer and her sister had ovarian cancer, it was suggested that we should all be tested to look for a possible genetic link. For that to be done we were referred to Southampton University Hospital and we decided we would all go together for the day. Despite the obvious difficulties, we all had counselling and decided we would have the tests. The result was that our mum has the *BRCA* 2 gene, but at eighty-five, she is fit and well. Her younger sister, who lives in Australia, was tested and was found to have the same gene mutation and when she had mammograms, they found a small cancer and she has had a lumpectomy. My older sister who had the cancer was positive but her twin sister was negative, and our other sister was negative. However, at the age of forty-six, I was told that I was positive for the *BRCA* 2 gene.

When I was asked how I felt about it I said, "Well, I don't feel any different. I obviously had the gene yesterday when I didn't know and I've got it today and I am more informed, but I haven't changed." What did change was that I would need to have breast screening regularly.

At Southampton they were doing a trial that compared mammograms with MRI scans. The breasts are more dense in younger women which makes it more difficult to see small abnormalities and there was the possibility that MRI scans would be better for screening younger women. I agreed to be part of the trial and had a scan straight away. The next day, I was at work in our local hospital when the phone rang. It was the breast surgeon who wanted to see me and a few minutes later I learned that the scan of the previous day had shown a lump. When a biopsy showed it was cancer I had a mastectomy.

I WAS NINE when my mother died of breast cancer. She was thirty-two when she was diagnosed and had a mastectomy, but I think she had a lump when she was pregnant with me and didn't do anything about it until after I was born. All I remember is that my mum stuffed her bra with cotton wool balls, but as a child, I never realised why. Thirty-seven years ago, cancer was not talked about and nobody explained it to me; now I wish I could talk to her and understand more of what happened. It's horrible not having a mum when you're growing up. Then my sister, at thirty-four, developed breast cancer.

Because of this family history, I had yearly ultrasound scans in my late twenties and after thirty I had annual mammograms. When I reached thirty-six and was due for the x-ray,

I noticed changes in my breast: the skin looked like orange peel and the nipple became inverted. The usual tests found a five centimetre cancer and two other tumours in the same breast, so mastectomy was the only option. Also, because of my family history, I was referred for genetic testing. A month later, I knew I had the *BRCA* 2 gene, and discovered there was a very high chance of developing cancer in my other breast. I had received very thorough counselling to prepare me for this possible news, and the counsellors couldn't have been more helpful, but it was still a shock and I cried. What bothered me even more was that I could be carrying a faulty gene that my daughter could have. However, she was only five years old and that could wait. Our first concern was to decide what I was going to do: I had a second mastectomy.

It is now twelve years since my mastectomy and our daughter is approaching her eighteenth birthday, which will have more than usual significance for her. She knows that I have the faulty *BRCA* 2 gene and that she has a fifty-fifty chance of carrying it too. A few months ago, the subject of cancer came up in conversation and she had a few moments of meltdown. "Will I get cancer because you've had cancer and Auntie P has had cancer and Nanna had cancer? Am I going to die of cancer?" She was really distraught.

I've known all along that we would have to face this one day, but all I could say to her was that I didn't want it to happen and we didn't know. At some stage, she will need to be counselled and make her own decision about being tested or not. If she is negative her family will not have to worry about the gene, but if she's positive it would be very different. She's too young to have the test at the moment and it's very rare for a young woman in her twenties to develop breast cancer, but she will have to decide about testing one day. Our daughter is very sensible and at the moment she's leaving it till she's older, but she will then have to decide. We don't know anyone else who has been in this situation. I was invited to join a group, but that sort of group was not for me. The counsellors at the Centre for Life, where they do the testing for the faulty *BRCA* 2 gene, are so good I'm confident they will know how to help her.

BECAUSE OF THE HISTORY of ovarian, as well as breast, cancer in the family, we all started ovarian screening and had an annual sisters' day out for ultrasound scans. One of the side effects of chemotherapy was that my periods stopped, but when they didn't restart after the chemo and I developed stomach pains, I saw the breast surgeon again. She was a lovely lady and, also, very forthright. Her advice was simple: "You've still got your ovaries, but they aren't doing anything now, so just get rid of them!" Well, it might have been a good idea, but I didn't do anything about it at the time; until, that is, I married my husband four years later. His previous wife had died of cancer and thinking of all that they had gone through together with her cancer I thought it wasn't fair on him that I should keep my ovaries when they wouldn't be doing anything useful and might pose a risk. I had the operation a few months after we were married. That removed one of the risks from the *BRCA* 2 gene, but I still need regular mammograms and breast checkups that are now done every eighteen months. At the time of my operation I did talk with a lady who had bilateral mastectomies because she was *BRCA* positive and I talked about it with the breast cancer nurse, but it was important for me to make my own decision.

THE SUBJECT OF GENE TESTING hadn't come up with my first breast cancer in 1997 because it was still early days for *BRCA* and routine testing of young women with breast cancer had not been introduced. When I had told them that my father's mother had died of cancer nobody had seemed interested; the focus then seemed very much on my mother's family which was not cancerous at all and I didn't yet know my grandmother's cancer had been ovarian. After my second breast cancer in 2012, I went for my regular smear and the gynaecologist asked immediately if I had been gene tested. When I said I didn't think I had, her reply was that I was behaving just like a *BRCA* person and should go for screening.

Seeing the geneticist focused attention on both sides of my family history. By now I knew that my father's mother had died of ovarian cancer in 1960. Dad was a smoker and died of lung cancer, but when a cousin investigated the family tree she found that my grandmother's mother, aunt and first cousin had all died of ovarian cancer, all on my father's side of the family, not my mother's. The older generation had apparently spoken of the family being 'riddled with cancer', but nobody had specifically talked about it – I think they felt rather cursed and of course 'women's things' were not for everyday discussion. Because of what we now knew, it seemed clear to me that I needed to be tested. My brother and five of my ten cousins have subsequently been tested too and so far, I am the only one who has the *BRCA* 1 gene.

For my gynaecologist there was no doubt about her subsequent advice: in her view, I should have my ovaries out because it could be life-saving surgery. She couldn't have put it much clearer than that. I had already experienced cancer twice and I was post-menopausal anyway; it was a no-brainer for me! Forty-five minutes of keyhole surgery, absolutely fine, and a week later I did a ten mile walk with my husband. Now I tell all my friends to do it. Then, of course, that left the question of my breasts: I had had breast cancer twice and didn't want it a third time – I wanted to have a double mastectomy.

My oncologist said I should wait three years because 'I was not out of the woods' from the 2012 cancer which was rather a blow. However, last year I got into a bad place mentally and was convinced my cancer was back so, at my next check-up, I asked if I could go ahead yet and he referred me for surgery. The surgeon was initially very dismissive – "I don't know why you want this surgery; it's going to be very unpleasant and it won't increase your life expectancy because breast cancer is now curable." He reckoned I had only a thirty percent chance of having breast cancer again and the surgery would give me three months of hell. My reply was that another breast cancer would give me a whole year of hell and I would prefer only three months, thank you very much. Back to see my oncologist and he agreed that the chance of another cancer was probably nearer fifty percent rather than thirty and, indeed, would only be curable if diagnosed early. I was quite clear that I wanted surgery and to remove the sword of Damocles hanging over my head. When I saw a plastic surgeon he was very supportive: it was a done deal, he gave me a date and six months ago I had bilateral mastectomies. My residual risk of breast cancer is now down to five percent.

Our two boys have finished university and they now know about the *BRCA* gene. Had they been girls, I'm sure they would have been more concerned about the implications for them of their mother having had breast cancer, what with all the attention in the press and social media. For the boys, I think it's been different; they were obviously worried about me, but the impact on them was less immediately apparent until I had the screening. The professional advice has been that the relevance for them is a slightly heightened risk of prostate cancer, a small chance of breast cancer and, more significantly, the implications for their children. When I decided on the mastectomies we explained the background and that the *BRCA* gene can pass through male members of the family and, again, they were very matter-of-fact about it. We have offered them the chance to see a geneticist and arrange testing anytime they want, if they want, but it's their call. If they have the *BRCA* gene they would probably be advised to have any children by IVF, so they can screen out the gene, but that would be a decision for them and their partners at that time. It's not urgent and we don't know what else will be discovered in the meantime; there are likely to be increasing numbers of our children's generation who will have the ability to screen out such illnesses through IVF as medical advances are made so it will become more normal. It is something they will do together with their partners and I hope it will be no big deal.

WHEN I WAS DIAGNOSED with cancer I was far more upset for my mum than for me. With any serious disease it is always harder for the person you live with than it is for you. My mum was devastated. She already had one daughter with cancer and now a second and it was from my mum's side of the family that the *BRCA* gene came, yet she was all right.

I had already had several operations in the past for other problems, unrelated to cancer, so getting breast cancer and needing another operation was just another thing that had to be done. I was confident that it could be dealt with and I didn't think it was going to kill me, and I'm still very sure of that. But for Mum it is very hard having already lost her mum, her dad, two sisters, a brother and daughter to cancer. That is why I say having the *BRCA* gene, cancer is a bit like measles in our family.

Mammy's poorly boobie

OUR DAUGHTER WAS ONLY FIVE when I was diagnosed with breast cancer, so we explained that Mammy had a poorly boobie and would have to go to hospital. The operation was done during the school holidays so she was able to visit me every day which she found quite exciting as she had never been in a hospital before.

When the dressings were removed, I was very upset. You look down and there's just the scar and nothing else; there should have been something there, but there wasn't. Your body's different and nobody else knows how you feel about that. And I didn't want my little girl to see me like that either. She always came in the bath with me, but when I came home from hospital, I locked the bathroom door. That upset her and she cried to come in. I told her that Mammy looked different now because her poorly boobie wasn't there anymore, but she still wanted to come in. When she did, she screamed and my husband had to take her out. However, the next day she returned to the bathroom door saying, "I want to come in the bath." This time she wasn't frightened. Sometimes, since then, she has asked about the scar and touched it, but she was never bothered by it again.

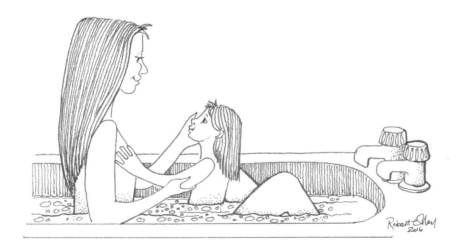

Win! Win!

I WAS PETRIFIED. Because I had breast cancer twice and had the *BRCA* gene, I had decided to have bilateral mastectomies. Now I was facing major surgery. The operation took eight and a half hours, but I needn't have worried; the result was wonderful. I had always had much bigger breasts than I liked and am now down to a size that I wanted to be; they took tissue from my tummy to enable the reconstruction of two new, smaller breasts and they managed to preserve my nipples. I was in hospital for eight days because one of the drains would not dry up, but a week after that, we walked half a mile down the road to our local Indian restaurant and back again. It was extraordinary – and a win-win all round. I had had a tummy tuck and a boob job! It was such a positive thing to do; I don't even think about cancer now and I don't regret it for a second.

Friends, a diary and follow-up

When Anabel was first diagnosed with cancer she took the approach that she would be told what she needed to know; she did no research, didn't need to know what drugs the oncologists were giving her and she didn't ask questions.

YOU DO NOT THINK ABOUT ANYTHING ELSE, at all, when you are diagnosed with cancer. Next, you get to the stage where you manage five minutes thinking about something else. Then gradually, gradually you get your life back when you don't need to think about it, but that doesn't happen overnight. I've always been a very positive sort of person and for me that took about six months – it's a lonely time as people really don't get it. I've never felt I was in the 'Cancer Club' and never wanted to go to support groups because I didn't want to admit to being in that club, although I realise having breast cancer is probably easier than some other cancers because it can be eliminated through surgery. My husband was enormously supportive and we talked about it at the beginning, but we are not a very talky couple and there's not much to be said once you're getting on with life again.

Friends were very important in getting through it – really, really important – because it's so nice to feel special. Writing a diary was also a help. There are times when you don't think you are getting better so being able to look back and see that you have made progress was very encouraging. The other important thing about a diary is to see, looking ahead, that it has lots of good events in it that happen to have a chemo session tucked in between, rather than just seeing a seemingly endless list of chemo appointments stretching ahead.

Finishing treatment was very scary. While you are being treated you are in the system, you are being checked all the time, all you are thinking about is the next treatment and getting through it, but then suddenly you are cast adrift. People think that's when you bring out the champagne, but no, no, no, no, that's when you have to get your head round the big picture. You are discharged from hospital, the professionals say 'Off you go, see you in three months' and you're on your own. Now it's up to you to face the paranoia that it could come back, and face up to getting your confidence and life back. Re-possessing your diary again was the scariest thing.

Over the next ten years I continued to have regular mammograms, which everyone else found reassuring, but I felt were nothing to celebrate. To me all they meant was that there was nothing to be seen rather than there was nothing there; my first cancer had not been visible on the x-ray they took after I had found the lump. Each mammogram also had another downside: we are very good at forgetting and we've gone back to normal living so, when the mammogram was due, it was a reminder that cancer did happen to me and, yes, there is a risk and I can't take life for granted; for several days beforehand it was a scary feeling. However, I am a test junkie who will have whatever is going and continued with the mammograms even though I set little store by them. I also saw my surgeon and oncologist at regular intervals and at ten years, they told me I was just a statistic, which was wonderful.

Chemotherapy

I SAW SOMEONE write on the internet that 'Chemo is awful, but it's do-able' which described it for me. You can do it, you can get through it and it really does all finish surprisingly quickly.

MY HAIR FELL OUT but there was no sickness, I didn't lose my appetite, I didn't feel tired, the steroids gave me an energy boost, so I did shopping and lots of cooking.

THREE DAYS AFTER the last chemo I did the local hospice's Christmas 'Turkey Trot', twice round the park. It was a crawl for me, not a trot, but I did it, and then went to bed. Cancer and chemo make you do daft things, but I did it because I didn't want to be ill.

I REALISE THAT EVERYONE is different and I have met some people whose chemo caused very few unpleasant side effects; for me, the bit that made it 'awful' was the nausea. The steroids were fine, but my hair fell out after the first cycle, much sooner than expected. I tried to wear a hairpiece, but it was too hot because I was still having menopausal symptoms and profuse sweating. Fortunately, whatever happens, it comes to an end.

THE ONCOLOGIST EXPLAINED when you cut into a loaf of bread and remove a slice there will always be some crumbs left. The aim of chemotherapy is to get rid of the crumbs that maybe left behind after surgery, which is a very good way of explaining the situation! The chemotherapy was in tablet form: two weeks on and one week off, and there were eight cycles like that. I had been warned about the possible side effects, but I was fortunate; the only effect I had was with my memory. I had panicky moments for no reason which started after the second lot of tablets. I would walk into a room and forget why I was there. At first, it was better during the week off, but later it was all the time. The memory problem was a bit ridiculous; I was quite useless on quiz nights at the pub! It did get better, mind, after the tablets stopped, clearing slowly till I was back to normal after about four weeks.

MY BIGGEST CONCERN was my hair. Losing my lovely long hair because of the chemotherapy would be awful and I was determined to do everything possible to keep it. If you lose your hair everybody can see it, you can't hide it and you can do nothing to control who knows you've got cancer. I had lost a breast, but people only knew because I chose to tell them. Doing some research, I discovered the 'cool cap' that could stop hair loss. My husband was more concerned that nothing should interfere with the treatment, but I told him, "It's not your hair, it's my hair and I want to keep it!" My hospital did not use the cool cap so I found another one with a good chemotherapy unit that did; they had a cool cap, nice biscuits and good coffee, so I went there. The cool cap wasn't bad, a bit noisy and a slight headache like being out in the snow, but it was bearable and it was my hair I was saving. The chemo was easier than I thought and I went home feeling fine, didn't feel sick, just a bit tired, became constipated, put on some weight, not bad at all. But, ten days after the first session the hair started coming out – not much to start with, but then lots and lots. A friend who was a hairdresser came round to see me and the look on her face told me everything, and I went upstairs to cry. I knew I would have to go for a wig. I really did not want to go to the wig shop, but another friend came with me and we had a laugh and I took a wig home but inside, I hated it. Monday morning came and I was dreading going to the school, but as I walked in, another mum said, "Hey, Debra, have you had your hair cut? It looks lovely," and I thought, 'Yes! I'm okay' and it made my day. If I could remember who she was, I would love to kiss her because after that I was different – and we forgot all about the cool cap.

I LOST MY EYEBROWS and eye-lashes, and my hair thinned a bit, but otherwise I sailed through chemotherapy without any problems and was back at work full time for the last two months. I had a lot of people praying for me at the time, so I believe this is why it went so smoothly.

BEING IN THE TRADE and being with patients on chemo every day, I knew what to expect and what the side effects could be. I took plenty of fluids and made sure I took all the medicines I was prescribed. The chemo did funny things. I got the days and nights mixed up. With the steroids I was on a high and couldn't sleep. If I took them any later than four o'clock I was doing the ironing at two o'clock in the morning. All I could do was sit all day in front of the television unable to concentrate and forgetting things – the nurses call it the 'Square-eyes-sore-bottom syndrome'. Fortunately, it passes.

When I lost my hair that was terrible, so I got my daughters to shave it all off; it was important that they be involved too. I had seen too many patients who were in tears: 'I've tried to save my hair, but it's all falling out'. I had long, blond hair and when the second cycle of chemo started it was coming out: in the shower, all over the pillows, on my clothes. It would have to go. The girls came round and we had a great time: first it went Mohican, then stripes, all sorts. We took photos; it was hilarious! After that, I wore a hair piece and we had fun with bands and scarves, trying to be creative, trying to lift the emotions. You've got to, you can't dwell on it.

I WAS VERY LUCKY with the chemo in that I was only sick once, although I did develop neutropenic sepsis that required emergency antibiotics and four days in hospital after the first cycle.

THE 'COCKTAIL' of chemotherapy drugs that was advised didn't sound like a Pina Colada to me, but they were the experts and you have to trust them. Having a friend with me when I saw the oncologist was a great help because when the side effects were explained, we actually giggled about it. Bright red hands, no hair, bald, mouth ulcers, sore gums. 'Oh! You'll look as pretty as a picture, won't you!' – but afterwards she cried for me. Another friend could not understand how I could joke about it to which I replied, "Well, it's a good job it's me that got the cancer then!" I think I was like this, partly, because there was no choice, but also because I knew there would be a whole medical team behind me to look after me.

I SHOULD HAVE HAD SIX CYCLES of chemo, but had only three. With each cycle I developed neutropenic sepsis and was so ill with the third cycle that the oncologist said she was worried they might kill an already cured woman. I was disappointed but, once again, there really was no choice. I was so tired it took another six months before I could return to work and it was a whole year before I felt anything like normal again.

THE CHEMOTHERAPY WAS AWFUL but I managed it, with the help of family and friends. It involved infusions every week for eighteen weeks and it knocked my diabetes absolutely up the creek! I wasn't eating, but my blood sugars were all over the place, despite stopping the insulin; I checked my blood sugars every four hours and we coped.

Although I knew what chemotherapy could be like, I had no conception of just how 'ill' you would feel. I was sick only twice on the night of the chemo; the steroids made it difficult getting to sleep, but after that, the rest of the week I was fine. What made the chemo so awful was the fatigue, sheer fatigue, complete exhaustion; it's hard to describe. One day I picked up a letter from the front door, walked to the lounge and simply didn't have the energy to open it! Fortunately, the oncologist had warned me about the fatigue so I knew it was 'normal' and I could be reassured that there was nothing else going wrong. When I was whingeing to the oncologist he would say, "I'm sorry I can't give you any assurance that it will get any better. It may actually get worse because of the cumulative effect of the drugs, but it will be worth it." Later on, I developed numbness of the fingers and toes, just at the finger ends to start with. It has improved, but it's a strange sensation, like sand in my shoes when I walk, and I do tend to drop things a lot. But the chemo finished eight months ago and the numbness is getting better and shouldn't be permanent.

Last week I managed about a mile round the lake with my son and tomorrow I'm going out with the walking group, for the first time since it all started, and I should manage maybe a couple of miles. Once again, it's helpful to remember what the oncologist said, that it may be two years before I recover completely from the chemo.

TO THE ONCOLOGISTS I WOULD SAY please organise treatments for us patients so they are arranged and coordinated properly so we spend as little time at hospital as possible: we have lives to get on with!

Cancer was the most positive thing that happened to me

"YOU'VE GOT A LUMP IN YOUR NECK," said my boss when I went into her office one day. I was at university studying biomedical sciences and was working in the microbiology laboratories of the local hospital. I had not noticed anything, but when she pointed it out it was obvious; it moved up and down when I swallowed and I could not understand how I had not seen it before.

The surgeon was quite dismissive, said it was just a lump in my thyroid and was quite sure it was benign, not cancer. Having a fine needle biopsy is a minor procedure, but the way it was done made it an unpleasant experience and, as the result showed, it did not obtain enough tissue to make a proper diagnosis. Despite this, no one suggested repeating it and as soon as my final exams were finished I had an operation to remove the half of the thyroid gland that had the lump in it. Unfortunately, nobody explained what the operation would involve, or what to expect afterwards, so that was an even more unpleasant experience. Then, to cap it all, when I asked to know the result of the histological examination, they discovered it was cancerous after all and I had to have the rest of the thyroid removed three weeks later. Nobody warned me my voice might be affected – the nerve to the larynx is very near the thyroid gland – so when I lost my voice completely two days after the second operation I thought I would never speak normally again. It did come back, six weeks later, but the stories I read on the internet were very frightening. Also, when the thyroid is removed the hormones it makes have to be replaced by tablets, but I was prescribed the wrong ones and felt awful. I had no energy, felt totally apathetic, just wandering along in a dream world, switched off and with no wish to do anything. My way of coping was to close down and leave everything to other people.

Our GP also recognised our dissatisfaction with the care I had received and decided to refer us to the thyroid cancer specialist team in Newcastle. Going to the cancer centre for the first time was a daunting, rather negative experience: I was only twenty and everybody else looked so much older and unwell. I was going to need some more treatment, with radioactive iodine, which I had never heard of.

The idea of radioactive iodine treatment is very simple. The thyroid gland needs iodine to make its hormones and takes iodine from food. If the iodine is made radioactive and swallowed as a tablet, any thyroid cancer cells left behind after surgery will pick up the iodine and the radioactivity will be carried into the cells to kill them. That was easy enough to understand and the idea of taking a tablet wasn't exactly scary, but getting my body ready for the treatment and actually having it was a bit different!

Before the treatment could start a low iodine diet was required for three weeks to get rid of the normal iodine in my body. A great way to lose weight, but pretty horrible – just fruit, meat and vegetables. No dairy products so it was green tea or black coffee, and no alcohol – but it was my twenty-first birthday and I didn't care, so I had one pint to celebrate!

While I was having the treatment, my parents stayed in an apartment near the hospital. Because of the radioactivity, you have to stay alone in a lead-lined room with strict precautions. Because the tablet is radioactive, everyone else evacuates the area and someone comes in with a container, takes out the tablet with a long stick to give it to you, and runs away. Then you've got to swallow this thing that everybody else is so petrified of, ingest it and sit there staring out the window thinking, 'This can't be right!' There was rubbishy TV and I had my mobile to call my mum, but nothing else. And my mobile was going to be destroyed when I left. At meal times, someone would shout at the door so I could move to the far corner of the room, then they would come in, put the plate down on the floor, walk away and shut the door. Only then could I pick it up, have my meal and do my own washing up. There was a kettle so I could make a hot drink and my parents did drop off some take-aways to be given to me, and I've never drunk so much water in my life! You need to drink water to flush the radioactivity out of the body and they come with a Geiger counter to check if you're safe to be let out! I was only there for two days and I had been warned what it would be like, but the isolation was still difficult to cope with.

After all that, I just went home and got on with life. My neck was quite swollen for several weeks and I had a very dry mouth. Then when the thyroid replacement tablets were being sorted out for the long term I felt very unwell, very low mood, no energy, lethargic, absolutely 'Ugh!' I was in quite a bad place for a couple of months and became quite angry at that point. Angry at life. Why me at my age? You ride the wave of the operation and get over that, but when real life resumes and you still feel crap, that's quite difficult. I did go back to work about a month after the radioactive iodine despite feeling pretty groggy. For me, work was important and gave me a focus to help my recovery. Still being at university was a great help because I was determined to do well. I wasn't just going to pass, I wanted to prove to everyone that I could do it. I put the cancer at the back of my mind and never once thought it might beat me. Obviously, I did contemplate my mortality more than most twenty-year-olds do, but I was actually at peace with that. If it was my time to go, to leave this earth, then fine, I was accepting of that, but so long as I'm here, I will do my best to enjoy myself and be good at what I do.

Having the cancer was life changing. Having cancer was the most positive thing that happened in my life; it was hugely motivating! It's changed my life. Everything that I have in my life now is the result of what happened to me then. I wouldn't change it for the world. If I could go back, I wouldn't choose to have thyroid cancer, but I wouldn't be a doctor now if it hadn't happened. The whole direction of my life is the result of having cancer.

I still hate going to the hospital appointments for checkups because I don't want to have to think about the cancer. It makes me angry to be reminded of 'Why me?' and what has happened. It's not because they might give me bad news: once you've sat in that chair and been told the worst news you could ever hear, nothing can be that scary again. As a young person, getting cancer can make you quite angry and despondent at times, but it's important not to let it define you. It doesn't define me: it has enriched me. Everybody is an individual and cancer is a very broad term with so many negative associations, but for a young person it can be really empowering. Don't let the bad times stop you going for the future.

Moles ... and more moles

ALL MY LIFE I HAD LOVED THE SUNSHINE and took every opportunity to sunbathe. It made me feel good and having a glowing suntan gave me confidence. I was a busy working mum of thirty-three with two lovely little girls, a devoted husband and a fantastic tan. Holiday tans don't last long and we only had one foreign holiday each year, so when I was seventeen, I started visiting a local beauty parlour. Soon I was addicted to the sunbeds. It was easy. It took only a few minutes, wasn't expensive and I felt great. What more could a girl want? Every day, twice a day I spent forty-five minutes on the tanning machine and went on using them regularly, even after I was married and the girls were born. Looking good with a really good tan was important; I looked good and felt good.

I had a few moles on my skin like lots of other people. However, one day I saw that one of them had started to change colour: it was darker than the rest and had obviously changed without me noticing. I went to see my family doctor. She agreed it looked different from the rest and suggested I should see a dermatologist. He agreed, too, and recommended that it should be removed and biopsied to make sure there was nothing going on. A week later, not suspecting anything, I went back for the results. The mole was not just a mole. It was a malignant melanoma.

Two weeks later I went in for the procedure and was told afterwards that they had removed 'everything'. The family doctor received a letter saying that the second operation had been complete and no more treatment was needed, but I would need follow-up appointments every six months. While it was reassuring to know they would see me from time to time, I was not too sure what they would be looking for. Should I be looking out for anything myself? Would some of my other little moles change colour, and if they did, would they be malignant too? Why check-ups every six months? That seemed a very long time to wait if another cancer was a possibility.

I had an anxious six months and it didn't help when, at my first follow-up, they removed another mole 'just to be on the safe side'. And then, after that, each time I went for a check-up another mole was removed – always 'just to be safe'. I was told that my moles were 'dysplastic' which meant that they had the potential of being a malignant melanoma. The medical name for my condition was Atypical Mole Syndrome or AMS.

Several months later the dermatologist noticed a mole on my left flank; she thought it was a strange colour so they removed it. I was at work and received a call to say I needed to go for the results. This one was cancerous too. After getting over cancer once I had to go through the whole diagnosis and shock of cancer again. This time the surgery was much more extensive, but I was fortunate that the lymph nodes did not have to be removed as well. Following the operation I was off work for a while, but was able to return to my previous job. I also started with the six-monthly check-ups again and, to date, I have had fifteen moles removed.

A few weeks ago I had my dermatology check-up, which was very positive. However, I do check my moles on a monthly basis and I sometimes feel like a ticking time bomb, but I tell myself 'Life is precious'. Having cancer certainly puts things into perspective, so I live my life to the full – and I've learned to feel good without a sun tan.

A change of lifestyle was needed

Paul was forty-three, a successful business man, flying round the world working for a big American high-tech company with teams in North America, Europe and Asia. Eleven years ago, cancer was diagnosed and life changed.

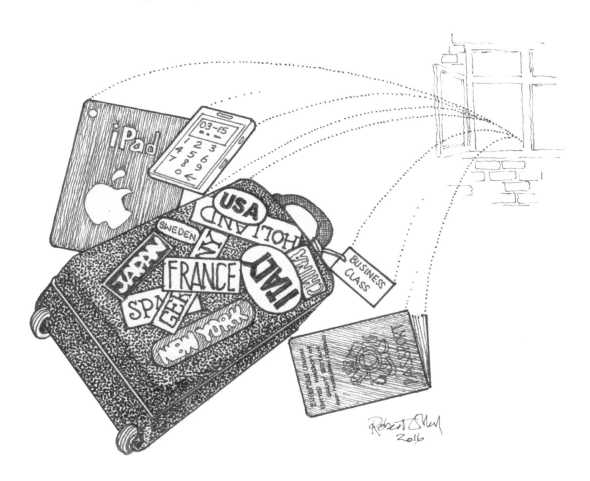

I T WAS WORK, WORK AND MORE WORK and I enjoyed it. It did mean being on the phone and on-line constantly. When I wanted to work, America was asleep and Japan had finished for the day – and it meant flying frequently in and out of Heathrow with only time for a shower and a change of clothes. But it was satisfying, and we had enjoyed three years near New York. However, I had a back problem, not helped by all those hours of flying and, after about six months, decided a trip to the doctor was needed. While there, I also mentioned a small lump I had noticed in my neck. It was only very small, about the size of a pea, and I could play with it when meetings became a little tedious. As the doctor examined me, her mood changed slightly and she called in a colleague; both agreed 'It's just a lymph node, nothing to worry about', but referral to a specialist was indicated. I had private health care insurance and investigations were swift. At this stage, with the reassurance I was given, I was not bothered; I was busy and my mind was on other things. I certainly didn't have any sleepless nights over it.

As you will have guessed, the lymph node contained cancer. Surgery followed quickly and they confirmed it was cancer of the tonsil involving the neck lymph nodes: an oral and full neck dissection was done.

How did it turn out? Well, I'll just say it was not a bundle of fun, but my wife was brilliant and she helped in every way imaginable. I was unwell with the chemotherapy; I had never been a cricket fan, but that was the year England played Australia in the UK in the Ashes and I watched every minute recovering from six cycles of chemo, lying on my front because of my bad back.

I also did my bit by creating a computer spreadsheet. Life became complicated because there were so many tablets to take, at the right time, fluids to drink, appointments to keep, things to do and it would be easy to get lost. Creating the spreadsheet gave me a sense of doing something to help myself. I could show people what I was doing, it offered a plan to beat the cancer, it gave me hope, something to build on, set targets to aim for and it provided a structure for each day. When six weeks of radiotherapy had finished it helped to count off the days till the side effects should begin to improve.

After that, it became what I guess was the usual post-cancer regime with regular checkups at the hospital. I was still tired and had lost twenty-five kilos and had to put on weight. I had to get out again and get fit and get used to the hair growing back. It took about three months before I could eat comfortably and much longer before there was any pleasure in eating – more than six months before it was worth paying to go to a restaurant. The mouth is dry and salty because either the saliva glands have been removed or those that haven't don't work properly; not a drop of alcohol for eighteen months, although I didn't miss it. My wife insisted that everything had to be 'healthy', but I craved something that was unhealthy! Chips! She continued working part time: we had someone in to clean, but she ran the home, looked after the boys, took them to school and me to hospital each day, and looked after me afterwards. Amazing. How she kept going I'll never know.

Our families lived too far away, but some of our friends were a great help. One in particular, a parent at school, brought round casseroles; so simple, so practical, but such a thoughtful thing to do. Some other friends arranged a party in the park when I finished my treatment – I was too knackered to join in the rounders, but it was a wonderful occasion. To our surprise the reaction of some others was different: even some close friends seemed not to know what to say and stayed away out of contact. I wanted to tell them that it was okay, but they weren't there.

For quite a while after the treatment finished, I wasn't up to doing anything much at all, certainly not work, but there was one thing that focused in my thoughts. I may not have talked about it, but I reached a decision, I made up my mind: a change of lifestyle was needed. In the background I wondered if the incessant pressure, the constant travel, the negative environment, hours each day with a big mobile phone pressed to my ear, and the stress of work had contributed in some way to the cancer. And, having time to reflect, I could see it was not the best for family life either: time with my wife and kids was more important. International travel would have to stop and I would work more normal hours. I would have to change my job.

There was time to think about it because recovery didn't happen quickly and, fortunately, my salary was secure and I had critical illness insurance cover. Although I had been a reasonably fit person before the cancer it took sixteen months from diagnosis before I was fit for work, both physically and psychologically. Now, for the past eight years, I have been very happy with a successful small company with a positive atmosphere, no international travel and more reasonable hours. During this time it has also been the teenage years for our boys and it has been great to have more time with them as they have grown up. It is rather sad that it took cancer to make me realise that I needed to change, but the outcome has been good.

Back near the beginning, when I was lying in bed recovering from surgery, I asked the surgeon what my chances were. When he said 'fifty-fifty' I was devastated, shaking; I hadn't realised it was that bad. At first I couldn't believe what he had just said and then I imagined the grim reaper waiting outside the door. Now, with hindsight, I think hearing that prognosis was a good thing because it stimulated us to do everything we could that might improve the odds. I have re-valued my professional and family life and that has brought us closer together.

Don't ask the lads at work

I WAS BLEEDING from the back end, so to speak, so I asked the lads at work, which was the daftest thing I could have done. I'm a pipefitter welder working off shore on the oil rigs in the North Sea. 'Oh, don't worry about it, it's just polyps' or 'It's just piles'. 'If it's not dark blood don't worry'. But it didn't go away. Typical man, it went on for over a year. Scared of what they might find I suppose. In the end it was my partner who pushed me: I wasn't happy, so I went to see the doctor. From him to the hospital and that was it. Bowel cancer.

The moment I heard that I went into a shell, like I had a spaceman's helmet on. I could see the surgeon's mouth moving, but I couldn't hear a word he said, numb with the shock. I hadn't suspected a thing. I thought I was bullet proof! He told me all the options including the worst case scenario if it had spread to my liver or lungs. There were questions I wanted to ask him, but I forgot – I should have written them down. Another friend had just died three weeks after being told he had it and I thought that was it for me too. I wasn't angry, just scared. At home I didn't talk about it. I tried to dodge the issue. I didn't want to upset my partner.

Looking back, I think I was being selfish. I was so taken up with me that I was not thinking about my partner's feelings. For weeks she was going through all her own thoughts by herself – her fears were probably worse than mine – she was my strength, but she needed me to console her. And it took someone else to tell me that. Later, I became angry and didn't realise that either. I started to get irritable, trivial things upset me. I even had road rage, effing and blinding at a bloke over nothing, and it was my partner who said, "That's not like you, it's your emotions coming out." Your biggest fear is not for yourself, it's for the children and your partner. You're more worried about their future without you being there for them. I've got six kids, the youngest sixteen and the oldest twenty-one. It was the youngster I was worried about. She really took it to heart. The night we told them I had cancer she didn't want to show her emotions and went to her older sister's for the night. Fortunately, by the time I had the operation we had sorted all that out and we were on a good time all together.

The scans had shown that the cancer was operable so I googled the surgeon to make sure he was good. He warned me that I would have a bag on afterwards as a precaution (an ileostomy), but if the bowel healed well, the bag would only be temporary, by which he meant nine to twelve months. I didn't actually understand what it would be like or how it would work, but I had confidence in him. He even came in on the Sunday evening to check we were all all right. The operation was great, with no pain, and I was only in hospital a week. They said I couldn't leave till I learned to do the bag, so I just got on with it. I surprised myself. You don't realise what strengths you've got until you are put in a situation like that. Doing the bag with no bother gave me a boost. When I first knew I had cancer I lost my confidence, but I've always been a positive person and I got the strength I needed from somewhere. At the operation they took away twenty-two lymph glands, seven of which were cancerous, and because of that, I needed chemotherapy – to mop up the 'crumbs' – so I concentrated on getting myself fit and was back to my usual self in a couple of months.

Life wasn't easy. I was made redundant soon after I was diagnosed and we struggled financially, but we've managed. Now that the ileostomy has been reversed I'm fit for work and raring to go.

Family matters

WHEN OUR BOYS WERE FOUR AND TWO I stopped work as a corporate stockbroker in the City to become a full-time mother, the intention being to take a few years out until the youngest was ready for full-time school. That plan changed two years later when I was thirty-eight and found a lump that was breast cancer. Not knowing what might happen in the future, I decided I wanted the boys to have as much of me as they could so that if the worst did happen they would have the best memories. My husband was working so we were lucky that there was no financial pressure. As the cancer had spread to a lymph node, I needed chemotherapy and radiotherapy after the lumpectomy and, with two small children, that was quite gruelling. We found a wonderful nanny who was quite extraordinary at judging my mood and what the boys needed, which kept it as seamless as possible for them.

IT WAS MY WIFE, my two boys, and the chance of recovery, no matter how small, that kept me going. When I was diagnosed, my wife was brilliant. She wanted to help, she needed to help, and part of that was to do practical things. She looked up everything. We changed my diet, cut out red meat, stopped alcohol, saw a nutritionist, consulted a homeopath, read books, took up yoga, and when we met the oncologist we made it clear, together, we wanted whatever treatment was available. They had described the cancer as 'aggressive' so we would be aggressive in return. If chemotherapy and radiation were required, that is what I would have, and the maximum dose possible. It might be tough, but we would go for it.

After the radiotherapy it was impossible to eat and the fortified drinks from the hospital tasted awful. My wife blended normal foods and fruit and I avoided a tube in the stomach which, I am told, would otherwise have been needed. She pushed me, she cajoled me, and she made sure I did what I needed to do. Without her, I have no idea how I would have managed.

I WAS FIFTY-TWO YEARS OLD when my cancer was diagnosed. My husband of twenty-five years had left me for someone else ten months before. With the two of my children who were still at home, we had just found a house to rent because the family home had been sold for a quick divorce. I needed to tell the children, so, starting with the eldest I 'phoned them and then went round to their house to tell them. Three of them accepted it, three didn't. One left home; she was twenty-three. Later, when we got together again, she said, "Mum, I couldn't bear to see what you were going through. My reaction was to run." Of course, in the event, they were all fantastic. The bond has always been there – it's never changed. Cancer was like an intruder that came into our life.

My two sons took it terribly. The youngest was at home with me. He was eighteen, but he looked after me. I remember one day when the chemo got the better of me, he said, "Come on, Mum, let me carry you to bed." But I said, "If you put your arms underneath me and carry me, I will never forgive you." But every night he would tuck me in. I tried to make a joke of it, but I had to let them be involved. My youngest daughter went withdrawn; her mood swings started. They couldn't open up to me and I didn't understand what was happening to me, so I couldn't help them. They should have had someone to talk to, they should have had counselling, but they didn't.

HAVING CANCER WAS A STRAIN on our marriage. My husband found it very hard to cope with, not being able to help his wife. When I was having the chemotherapy everything was out of his control and he couldn't do anything about it. He is quite a controlling person, in a good way. He likes everything to go right and that wasn't happening. He wanted to mollycoddle me, cups of tea, cups of coffee, wanted me to rest. He thought there wasn't anything he could do, but in fact he was a massive, massive help.

The hardest for him was when I lost my hair. I did not want a wig so wore a bandana instead, and my little girl wore a bandana when we went out, just like her mam. If I felt comfortable without anything on I would just take it off. It wasn't till after I had finished all my chemo and we sat down and talked a bit more that I realised that my husband had really struggled with the hair loss. When we went out and I got in the car he used to say, "Have you forgotten your bandana?" and I would say 'No'. Looking back, it was his way of trying to persuade me to wear something because he felt uncomfortable. It's okay for men with no hair, but for ladies walking round with no hair, people look. For me it wasn't a problem: it's just hair and it grows back. But for my husband it was a major factor.

THE TENSION WAS TERRIBLE AT TIMES and when I went home, I sometimes took it out on my husband because he was the only one there. We were so busy worrying and looking after our daughter we never had time to talk together, and I didn't want to show my feelings and let him see how scared I was. I don't think people realise the emotions you go through and how it is so easy to hurt the ones you love when it gets difficult, just when you should be helping each other. We have since learned that some marriages do not survive this sort of trauma; fortunately our marriage has, as well as our daughter.

I HAVE FINISHED MY CHEMO!!!!!! I just want to thank my children and grandchildren for helping me get through it.

ANOTHER ISSUE FOR US, of course, was the tamoxifen. The oncologist knew I had lost my son and knew I was so desperate for another child, but with tamoxifen and chemo you are not advised to fall pregnant, so she suggested I could have some eggs stored for when I had finished the tamoxifen. But by the time that happens I will be forty-three and that would be a bit old for me to start having another baby.

Looking back it was all a lot of pressure and all I could think of was that I needed to get the chemo started because I already had a child. There's never enough time to think about these things when they happen, but it would definitely have been helpful if the surgeon had told me about storing eggs rather than waiting to be told by the oncologist. If I had known about it then, I would have done it. By the time I did find out it was too late, because I was desperate to start the chemo and was worried that a delay might be harmful. Medical people may think it's too much information to give when you're diagnosed, but for young women it could be helpful.

The desire to have another child was always there. Even when I was having the chemo I thought about it. I wondered if I was being unrealistic. I knew I couldn't talk about it with my husband because the answer would be point blank NO. He would rather have his wife than another baby and he didn't want to take any chance on the cancer coming back because of the hormones. He feels awful for saying 'no', but he needs a wife. For me, the feeling has never gone away. I know people say 'You've got one, you have to be grateful', but I had my life mapped out in my head and it was always going to be with two children.

About six months after the chemo I felt strong enough to take the world on again so I started to think about the tamoxifen. I know I need to take it because it's part of the treatment and I cannot take the risk of stopping it. The risk may be small, but I had had my other breast removed because of the very small risk of getting a second cancer on the other side, so I could not stop the tamoxifen. Scary. The risk of the cancer coming back is a big fear that every person who has had cancer knows. I still want another child, but I've learned to look at life differently. I try not to plan ahead too much, try to be grateful for what I've got. In the end, you have to learn to cope.

I think I am the sort of person who needs to understand why things happen. I was very fit, ate all the right foods, had never smoked and was not a drinker. I am still looking for the answer. However, my feelings now are totally different from before. Life is a gift. My time with my little girl is precious.

A FEW YEARS AFTER THE CANCER, on a night out clubbing, I met my wife to be and we married a year after that. Anxious to start a family, we became worried when nothing happened and went to see our new doctor. He looked uncomfortable as he read my medical history and we knew something was amiss. "Did nobody ever explain that because of your cancer treatment you will not be able to have a family?" No, they hadn't. What a bombshell! I felt terrible because I had let my lovely wife down. When we had recovered from the shock we explored all the possibilities: donor insemination, fostering, adoption, but at every turn we were rejected. Although I was in long-term remission my future could not be guaranteed. It was my fault and nothing could be done. To our surprise, six months later a telephone call came out of the blue. It was the fostering and adoption social worker

44

who wanted to review our case. A little girl was in need of a home – and we became her lucky, long-term foster parents. What joy, the centre of our universe.

WE HAVE TWO SONS. When their mother was dying they were clearly very upset, but I said to them that it was up to them, but your mum would rather you remembered her as you knew her, and they did not come to visit for a couple of months before she passed away. That was her wish and they honoured that. When it became clear that she was dying they were going to come home, but it all happened so quickly they didn't get home in time. Our youngest, a chemistry and physics school teacher, is very quiet and says very little, but after the funeral I realised it had hit him very badly. Our oldest boy works in Dubai for a major car company. When we told him of the diagnosis he was very concerned, but living abroad and seeing us less he seemed to cope quite well. We had said not to rush back home, life must go on and we were going to be very optimistic. At the funeral he was the rock that kept his brother and me together.

I took a year out of my life
to save my life

EVEN BEFORE THE CANCER STARTED FOR ME people used to say, "Oh my god, it's turned my life upside down," and I would suggest, "Try to think of it this way: put your life on the shelf, and when you're ready and everything is all finished, get it down again, bring your life back and get started again." So, when it happened to me that's what I did. I parked my life in the garage and when treatment was done I got it out and now I have started driving again.

I worked for a private company that provided cancer chemotherapy for people at home rather than at hospital. My job was to visit them at home, take blood samples before and after every cycle of treatment, telephone the results to the oncologist and keep in regular touch throughout their treatment.

As I was over fifty I had received two appointments to go for a mammogram, but I was too busy to go; patients come first and there wasn't time for me to have a mammogram. But then I started feeling tired. No symptoms, lumps or bumps, I just decided it was time I tried looking after myself and asked for a mammogram – just a gut feeling. When I had the mammogram the doctor called me in straight away for an ultrasound and an aspiration biopsy, and then told me to go back in an hour for the result. I was at work that day and had taken time off to get the mammogram. Back at work, my manager said, "You're not going back on your own, I'm coming with you," but I said, "No, you're not." I would face it on my own whatever it was going to be. The MRI scan showed another tumour in the same breast; I needed a mastectomy as soon as possible.

The surgery happened fast, the next week, but that was okay. I couldn't get my head round it, but that didn't matter. I had to get it all done as quickly as possible. Back home, I recovered fine. I just ignored it: 'Keep going, you'll be all right'. I took two weeks' holiday for the mastectomy and then went back to work.

Six cycles of chemotherapy were needed which my colleagues gave me at home, but being on the receiving end, I soon discovered what chemo could be like: a rollercoaster of physical symptoms and emotions. It seemed I was on a fast moving train and didn't know which stop to get off. Only now, quite recently, do I feel I have regained control of my body and my life. Part of that has been to have breast reconstruction. It's all to do with getting back self-confidence and trying to regain the normality that was before the cancer.

46

It's not just women either: I have looked after two men with breast cancer who needed mastectomy and one of them has had reconstructive surgery.

Nine months after going back to work, I was made redundant. After all I had been through there was no way was I going to sit at home and claim benefits so I found a completely different job, working in a care home. Now, after two eventful years, I am returning to my old job helping others who need chemotherapy too.

A mother's story

Joyce's only daughter was nearly eighteen when she was diagnosed with a rare cancer. During treatment, her daughter nearly died.

I HAVE NEVER ASKED MYSELF why I ran away when Rachel nearly died. Looking back, I think it was the fear. For the first time in all those months, I really thought she was dying and I was taken over by a total panic. Maybe some other mothers have the same reaction when something like that happens. I don't know.

Our daughter was diagnosed with something very rare that we had never heard of, a supracellar intracranial germ cell tumour. It was just before her eighteenth birthday. After what we thought was successful treatment, when Rachel went for the result of the two year follow-up MRI scan, the news was not good. "I'm afraid the cancer has come back. We'll have to give you stronger chemotherapy." By this, the oncologist meant that the drugs would kill her bone marrow and that meant Rachel would have to have some stem cells taken away to be frozen and given back to her after the chemo. When you think about what can be done now it's quite amazing!

We knew this treatment was going to be much harder: the oncologist actually told us that not many people survived it. Rachel, and all of us, knew she might die from the treatment. There was no point in bluffing; we had to be realistic. Rachel never talked about it, but we made sure that she knew we would be there for her all the way. In reality that meant I stayed every day and night with her when she was in hospital, sleeping by her bed on the sofa bed. Not that I got much sleep! You meet the other parents in the kitchen and talk about their treatment. For most of them their children were not going to survive and you want to help them as much as you can. I still remember those bairns and see their faces. At night, when the nurses were busy, we watched the drips and when the alarms went off we went up the corridor to tell them, whether it was your bairn or somebody else's. When they were sick, we took them to the bathroom. We were all in it together and when some were obviously very ill, it could be very scary and you had to keep remembering that everyone is different and focus on your own child.

Unfortunately, Rachel had an unexpected reaction when they put the stem cells back in. I was with her when she said she didn't feel too good. Then she collapsed. In seconds the room was full of people. Up to this point I had managed to keep it together; I was exhausted but had kept going. I'd been strong for our Rachel, but this time I fled. Rachel looked as if she was dying. I ran out of the ward and out of the hospital into the nearby park. Fortunately, a social worker followed me, helped me to calm down and go back. Rachel was resuscitated, transferred to intensive care and survived. She needed more chemotherapy, more stem cells and more radiotherapy and each time I was terrified.

After the first treatment and Rachel was fine again we thought the cancer had gone and she was cured, but when it came back a second time we lost our confidence. I still fear it now, sometimes, and wonder about the future, but a few weeks ago she was given the all clear once again. We've still got our Rachel.

I think it was meant to be

*I'm young, only twenty-nine, and I do sometimes wonder
what life would have been like without the cancer.*

WHEN I WAS FIRST DIAGNOSED I never imagined the amount of treatment I would have to have. Altogether, what with going backwards and forwards to the hospital, surgery, chemotherapy, radiotherapy, catching infections, all the tests and appointments, the treatment took nearly two years. Then, less than two years after all that finished I was diagnosed again! That was just awful. The tumour I had in the first place was very rare and I had been told that it rarely came back so I didn't even think about that possibility. I had no idea that would happen.

When they told me I would have to have the same treatment all over again but with different drugs that would be even harsher than before, I was really, really frightened: if it had come back, despite all that treatment, would they be able to get rid of it this time, and how did I know it wouldn't come back yet again? I was also scared because I knew how poorly I had been with the treatment the first time and I knew I would feel even worse this time. They said I would need a 'stem cell transplant', but I hadn't a clue what that was. They explained it all, but if you're not medical you don't really understand. I was not looking forward to it at all!

I got through the chemo and then had the stem cells and it was then that I had a reaction. I was sitting up in bed in the hospital and said to my mum, "I feel a bit faint, I feel a bit funny." The next thing the doctor rushed in and I said, "I think I need some more hydrocortisone," and then collapsed. That's all I remember until I woke up a few days later, not knowing where I was. It had been septicaemia and very serious, but I was lucky. I can laugh about it now, but it wasn't funny for my mum and dad when it happened. My mum was very frightened by it all. Mind, afterwards she was dead proud that I knew that I needed more hydrocortisone! When they told me I would need the stem cells a second time you can imagine I was terrified, but there were no problems and it was all okay.

My friends were great; they all kept coming to visit me at home and in hospital. I was frustrated that I couldn't do what they were doing, but there was nothing I or anybody else could do about it. I couldn't get on with my life, but I wasn't jealous of them; in any case half the time I was asleep or out of it with morphine and didn't even know they were there. It was horrible. I did miss out – but I've made up for that now!

I started work when I left school at sixteen, but soon started getting headaches and all sorts of hormonal problems and hadn't a clue what was going on. Unfortunately, it took the local hospital two years to work out what the problem was. I was not angry at the time. However, after I had finished all the treatment, I was angry, very angry because if they had found it when I first went, when I was sixteen, I might not have had to have all that extra treatment. I went through the mill and that should not have been necessary. The treatment I received, though, was wonderful. The oncology staff were brilliant and really looked after me. Absolutely fab.

After the first time I wanted to go back to work, but still recovering from all that had happened I wasn't really ready so the CLIC Sargent worker at the hospital suggested I could try some voluntary work. She took two of us to the CVS (Council for Voluntary Services) where they had a file of different places needing volunteers. The first one I saw was a place called Cancer Connections and that seemed interesting. I had done a Modern Apprenticeship in supply and accounts at a supermarket head office before I was poorly and they needed a volunteer in the office. When I visited it was great: friendly, full on, lots of people to meet. I loved it so I stayed!

It took a long time to get back to work the second time. The chemotherapy left some deafness, the radiotherapy to my brain affected my memory and I lost my confidence: I can remember everything about my childhood, but not new things since my treatment, so I felt embarrassed about going somewhere new where they wouldn't know me and might not understand. If I'm asked to do something, I have to write it down so I don't forget. If I went to a different employer that could be a problem, but at Cancer Connections, I knew I would be all right.

My life would have been completely different if I hadn't had cancer. I still have to take lots of tablets and still have scans, but they are less frequent now. I wouldn't have chosen the treatment I had to have, but I'm here, fit and well, and I certainly wouldn't have been working here at Cancer Connections with so many lovely people. Looking back, it's funny, because when my tumour came back for the second time and I had to have all that treatment again, I had the support I needed all around me where I was working. I think it was meant to be.

What shall we tell the kids?

"PEOPLE CAN DIE FROM CANCER, CAN'T THEY?" That was our eight-year-old son as we sat round the table one evening. Then, after a few moments' thought, came the next question: "Mum, can you marry again?"

All through my cancer diagnosis and treatment our boys were ten and eight. We did not hide the cancer from them, but we didn't make a big deal of it. We told them Dad had cancer which would need some treatment and I don't think they ever saw me upset. We called it 'cancer' and did not shy away from using the word, although we didn't use it a lot. They would have heard it before and knew it could be serious, but at that age, it didn't seem to trouble them. Having said that, there were times when we would be talking about it and I would see them looking at me and I often wondered what they were thinking. That evening I found out! Since then, Dad has got better and he's still here and the boys are at university, so there has been little need to talk about it, although they do call me 'Turkey-neck' sometimes because of the surgery and radiotherapy.

MY FOUR-YEAR-OLD was too young to talk about it, but he often came to our room in the middle of the night to see if I was still there. The six-year-old had just found a verruca on his foot which was brilliant, because he got the idea that he had something on his body that was not very nice, but it could be treated with repeat medicine. We explained that I had a 'verruca' under my skin that needed different treatments and in this way he could grasp the concept in a low-key sort of way. We never used the word cancer, although we did worry that they might hear it from someone else. About six years later it came up in conversation and I said, "Of course, I had cancer," and they were absolutely dumbfounded because they had never picked it up. They remembered I had been ill and didn't mind that we had not told them. When I had cancer the second time, fifteen years later, it was completely different and we were very up front with them, which is what they wanted.

MY CHILDREN were five and seven years old and we wondered what to say to them. We decided to explain that Mummy was getting another mole removed, but we didn't go into me having cancer. As my girls got older, I did start talking to them. They were amazing. In their own way they seemed to understand and supported their mummy, although it was a few years before they were old enough to understand what cancer really was. To help them understand what was happening to me, and to help them not be frightened by the word cancer, I took the girls with me when I went to Cancer Connections; while I was having a therapy they had fun and enjoyed going. They even started to do fundraising and every penny went to charity.

WE KNOW that children are resilient and books advise that children should be prepared, but our grandchildren are only six, five and six months and our children do not want them to know yet. So, as far as they know, their grandad has a bad back. However, when we went out recently and I couldn't play with them the oldest asked, "When are you going to get fit again?" It was all I could do to hold my tears back and say, "We hope very soon with the help of the tablets I'm taking." Next time he went shopping with his mum, he bought something for his grandad's back.

THE GIRLS WERE AT HOME with my mam when my husband died, but they didn't know what was happening. Libby was only eleven months and Eleanor was four, and although that was five years ago they still do not know their daddy died of cancer. When Steven was dying, I had thought a lot about what I would tell them and I'd discussed it with my mam. On the day Steven died, when I returned from hospital my mam said that she would pop out to the shop for a while so I could have some time with the girls. Libby was sitting on one knee and Eleanor was on the other and I said, "You know that Daddy had a poorly tummy and the doctors couldn't make Daddy better. Well, God has made Daddy better, but he's had to go to heaven to be better."

"Right, but can he come back down now?" was what El wanted to know.

I explained that he couldn't because he had to stay there, otherwise he would get poorly again. "He's healthy there and he can see us, but he can't be with us." Eleanor missed her dad terribly and from time to time they both ask if people can come back from heaven to see us; when we went on holiday the year after and they went on the aeroplane they thought they might see him.

The girls have never questioned the word 'cancer' and have never asked, "What is cancer?" I have never used the word cancer with them because there is so much about it all around, but it doesn't always result in death and I don't want them to be frightened by it. It's an adult thing to be terrified by cancer and I don't want them to worry about it. Her daddy dying did not frighten Eleanor, but she was a daddy's girl and she misses him every day. Now that Libby is five, she has started asking about Steven all the time. The children had a giant snail at nursery that died and went to heaven. Then my mam's dog died and went to heaven, and then there was her other nanna who died as well, and she has a list of special people who are in heaven. The snail, the dog, her nanna and Daddy Steven. That's her way of remembering him. Children are wonderful aren't they?

Surgery was not for me

WE WERE HAVING LUNCH and I needed to tell my husband what I had decided. The breast cancer that had been treated seven years before had come back. Since then, we had been to the hospital many times and had seen numerous specialists. Now their advice was that I should have major surgery to remove the metastases that had grown in my liver. After weeks of changing my mind, sometimes almost every hour, I had decided. I was not going to have the operation. I would take my chances and if I lost ten years of my life, then so be it.

My husband, Will, thought about it and then replied lovingly: "Anything can happen to anyone at any time and there is nothing that can be done about it. But, for you, there is a chance of doing something. I'm sorry for being selfish, but I want those ten years with you." A few days later, we met a dear friend of my late mother with whom we had kept in touch since both my parents had died. I felt I could talk with her and asked what she would do in my situation. "I'm eighty years old and at my age I wouldn't bother with surgery, but you're only sixty. You should have it done."

The reason for not wanting surgery was simple: I was terrified of not waking up after the anaesthetic. Although I had worked as a nurse all my life and had looked after many patients having operations big and small, and knew that modern surgery is safe, I was convinced that I would die if I went ahead with surgery. I think that was why I suggested lots of other reasons why it should not be done. For a start, Christmas was coming and we could not disappoint the family; it would have to wait till the new year. And then, possibly not at all. Then there would be a large scar that my husband wouldn't like and he would go off me, but his reply was, "I went off you three months after we married, but I'm still here thirty-two years later! Scarring doesn't matter, you are still you and that's what matters." Also, there would be how to manage after the operation. I might not be able to get upstairs for a few weeks when I returned home. But he had made plans for that, too. Then they might want me in hospital on my birthday – "So, we'll borrow your mum's birthday instead and we'll celebrate a few days before." Will answered all these excuses, and I knew they were feeble, but there was nothing that could stop me being frightened. In the end I said yes, but was still not sure.

When the day came, I put on my best make-up and said nothing. Inside, I thought I would never see my home again, but I would go to the hospital, for everybody else's sake. However, when I got there, I changed my mind again. The anaesthetist came to see me first and Will explained about my fear of not waking up. He spoke at length and was very pleasant, but I was not convinced. After he left, the surgeon came in. "What's all this about not wanting surgery? I'm glad you feel fit, otherwise we wouldn't do the operation. I understand why you are afraid, but you must realise that you will die of the cancer if we do not attempt surgery. It's up to you." Of course, I had been told this before, but not quite like this. As I left the room to go to the operating room, Will said, "Remember 'I'll Be There'" – the song by the Jackson Five that was 'our' song when we first met as teenagers. When I arrived in the operating theatre, I still had my make-up on.

The operation took seven hours and I woke up in the critical care unit, feeling much better than expected. The surgeon came to see me and explained that the surgery had been successful, all the cancer had been removed and a scan during the procedure had not shown any other tumours. Ten days later, I was home and scans over the following months were clear; I was in remission once again. I will be eternally grateful to those who treated me.

No matter how many times we say that cancer will not change our lives, or how much we may not want it to, it does, and it certainly changed mine. If it had not been for the cancer in my breast nine years ago, I would have continued doing the job that I loved with colleagues who had been such good friends. If it had not returned in the way that it did, my husband and I would not have had long months of uncertainty and anxiety that, at times, seemed almost to paralyse our lives. If I had not needed surgery, I would not have spent months trying to face my worst fear. I do blame cancer for all of this and, sometimes, I am still very angry. Talking and working with a counsellor has been a great help. After all, I am still here and Will has had the first two of those ten years he wanted with his wife.

I was lucky

Audrey, a retired nurse, thinks she was very lucky:
it was a blood test that found her cancer.

TWO YEARS EARLIER, I was investigated for anaemia and quite a large, but benign, ovarian cyst was found. The gynaecologist recommended a blood test every six months to keep an eye on the cyst. The test was for a substance called CA125 and between two of the tests, it went up from seventeen to over 200 and that suggested cancer. I didn't have any symptoms except that there had been a heavy feeling in my tummy. Nothing else. I felt very fit. If it hadn't been for the blood test, I wouldn't have gone to the doctor. All sorts of scans were done and then a laparoscopy, and that showed I had 'primary peritoneal cancer'. Urgent surgery was needed and that was organised very quickly. It involved a full hysterectomy and cutting out as many of the nodules as possible. Unfortunately, I was very unwell halfway through and they could not finish all they wanted to do, so chemotherapy would be necessary as well.

Recovery after the operation was hard going. I seemed to be in hospital longer than anyone else, but I went home after nine days. I was on my own at home. I had the phone by the bed, the boys live nearby and I have lots of good friends who called, brought soup and helped in different ways. Mind, phone calls! They're lovely, but they can be exhausting. When you're feeling tired and want to sleep you're very grateful, but sometimes you really do want to be left in peace!

I thought I knew what chemotherapy would be like, but I had not anticipated the profound fatigue that followed. Despite this, I didn't stay in bed: I made sure I showered and dressed every day – and I've nearly worn the sofa out resting on it so much every day for five months. Ending the chemotherapy was a complete relief.

Going for the blood test every few months is a worrying time, but knowing the results of the CA125 – the 'marker' that tells the cancer activity – is always helpful. What was really reassuring, was when I first started the chemo and the oncologist showed me the graph that showed the CA125 had fallen by seventy percent: he said he'd never seen it fall so fast before. Now the thought of cancer isn't there all the time anymore. If it comes in the night, I read a book and it goes away. As each day passes, I feel better and can do more, and before long, I really will feel it's been worth it.

We talk together much more now

George was working as a production manager on the shop floor
of a heavy engineering company when an unusual type of bladder cancer was diagnosed.
Successful treatment avoided the removal of his bladder, but when the same cancer
affected a kidney, major surgery was required.

IT'S BEEN EIGHTEEN YEARS since it all started and you might think we'd got used to it, but when the check-up is due, we both get tense and start bickering. Every little pain, you go to the doctor for reassurance. We never forget that at the very beginning we were told it was an aggressive type of cancer, and it has shown that by coming back once in the bladder and in a big way in the kidney. However, the bladder treatments, the surgery and the chemotherapy have been successful: I've been clear of cancer for more than ten years and I'm still here. It's been hard at times for both of us, in different ways, but it's brought us closer. We talk together much more now, we like nothing better than going to stay at our caravan in the countryside, and we take a lot of pleasure just being together.

When I mentioned passing dark urine and a little blood the doctor referred me to a specialist immediately, and a bladder examination showed a patch of what they later called 'cancer in situ' in my bladder. Apparently, this could be an aggressive form of bladder cancer that could kill me and would probably need the removal of my bladder at some stage, but they said they would try weekly BCG bladder washes to start with. I thought BCG was for tuberculosis, but apparently it's good for bladder cancer, too. The washes were straightforward and although there was another tumour in the bladder a few months later, the regular treatments over the next few months did the trick and my bladder was free of cancer.

Six years later, when they did the usual cystoscopy check, I could see something on the screen that looked like a small sea anemone. Urine drains from the kidney to the bladder through a tube called the ureter and this new tumour was just by the opening of the ureter which they told me did not look quite normal. Tests showed that I had the same sort of cancer in the ureter and the kidney as I had in the bladder and the treatment would have to be major surgery. The operation was done by the keyhole approach (the professionals call it laparoscopy) and I came home four days later. The hospital was testing a new system by which the patient went home quickly, still with a catheter in and staples in the wound, and I have to say, it was much better being at home. I was off work for two or three weeks, and then I was back on the shop floor supervising the production of refrigerated trailers. At the hospital, they had told me I might need some chemotherapy, so the thought of cancer was there in my mind all of the time; getting back to work, the normality of it, gave me something to hang on to.

At home, it was different: my wife was worried and very emotional and we had a sixteen-year-old son. Right from the beginning, it had been that word. Even though the thing in my bladder was tiny, they said it was cancer. When it came back in my kidney, we kept it largely to ourselves. We didn't want to talk outside the family about it, but our son knew it was cancer and he's not daft. He cried in front of his mother, but not with me. The hospital recommended chemotherapy, because, although they reckoned the operation had removed the kidney and the cancer completely, they wanted to make sure by mopping up any remaining microscopic particles. Knowing I would need chemotherapy was not good and there was also the worry about the other kidney: would it be able to cope and what would happen if the cancer spread? However, when we saw the oncologist, he said, "What are you two looking so worried for?" We felt a lot better: if he wasn't worried, why were we? It was a weight lifted off both of us. I told personnel at work about the chemotherapy and they were very good about it. It flattened me a couple of times, but they let me work when I felt up to it and I managed to work most of the time while having the chemo. The cancer didn't interfere with me doing my work and being able to work was a great help. However, for my wife, who was at home all the time because of her rheumatoid arthritis, it was very hard. I had companionship at work, but she was alone all day. Sunday was our family day when everyone came round, but in the week, they were all busy and at work.

After the kidney operation, I continued with the regular cystoscopies and after a couple of years it must have shown something that caused some concern which led the surgeon to suggest it was time to have my bladder out. He explained the various options, but I was not at all keen, so he agreed to take biopsies from different parts of the bladder to see exactly what the situation was – 'bladder mapping' they called it. The biopsies were all normal which was very reassuring, but the surgeon was still concerned. My view was that I did not want to lose my bladder unless it was absolutely necessary. If he was worried, the BCG had worked the first time so why couldn't I have some more BCG now to protect the bladder for the future? And that's what we did. I had BCG bladder washes every three months over the next three years. I still have bladder examinations every six months and at my last check, a few weeks ago, my bladder was fine.

It seemed so easy

Leaving school at fifteen, Patricia joined the police service as a cadet and then went on to serve in the force for twenty-eight years. During this time, she took advantage of a scholarship for university and qualified as a lawyer. When she retired from the police service, she started a second career as a legal advisor to the magistrate courts. Three years after her second retirement, invasive bladder cancer was diagnosed.

ENJOYING THE PLEASURES OF RETIREMENT, I had already gone through the process of understanding where I was in my life. While I was hoping for more years of retirement, because they are supposed to be long and sun-filled, I realised that there was nobody whose life would be very much the worse without me. I have an uncle and several cousins with whom I am close and we get on very well, but they have their lives and if I disappeared from the scene, it would not make a great difference to them in any practical way, and that was a very comforting thought. I had a task in front of me that I had to do as best as I could and I didn't tell anybody I had cancer for a very long time.

Although she had to explain that I might lose my bladder, it was the nurse specialist who was most helpful. By then, of course, I had been scrounging around on the internet and knew this might happen and, encouragingly, it seemed that the operation 'cystectomy' had a good survival rate. Also, I had read about radiotherapy and learned that if that treatment was not successful, I would need to have the bladder out in any case; surgery seemed to be the best idea. By the time I met the oncologist, I think he understood that I had already decided. However, beyond that, I did not wish to think. Whatever followed, I would cope with it.

At times, I did wonder if I had not understood properly, but I was aware that I might die because of the cancer and that was enough; I would simply take advice and follow it. When staff explained what the operation would involve I didn't really listen, because I didn't need to know. If I have no choice I am very good at coping and, as a result, I had very little feeling about it.

Three cycles of chemotherapy were advised first, which I neither looked forward to, nor enjoyed. It made me ill and I wasn't used to being ill. However, there is always a bright side to these things. It was summer and each time the chemo was finished, I bought a cup of WVS coffee and sat outside in the sun to wait for the taxi, and that was so pleasant! It was a joy to be driven rather than driving oneself. These little things get you through the bad bits.

The operation was done and my bladder was removed. I cannot recall having any pain and it seemed to take forever to be allowed home: I was in hospital for thirteen nights. Discharge was delayed because the hospital staff were very concerned about how I would manage at home on my own, but in the end I lied and said that I had made arrangements myself. In reality, my ninety-year-old aunt came to stay, which was invaluable as she was able to make cups of tea and answer the door. With my bladder removed, I had a 'urostomy' instead of a bladder, together with a bag on my tummy that I had learned to look after while in hospital. After that, life went on. It took a while to recover, as one had to learn what was possible and what was not; gardening was my joy, but there could be no digging anytime soon. It was winter and I just took my time. Having a urostomy has been a problem only very occasionally. I carry a few things with me just in case there is a leak, but it seldom happens.

I did tell my aunt and cousins about the cancer when I got a date for the operation because I needed to nominate next of kin, but I didn't tell anyone else until it was all over. At that stage, I told friends and neighbours who could then do all their 'oohs' and 'aaahs', but there was no longer anything to worry about as they could see that I was better. It was easier for them and easier for me doing it that way.

Now, cancer and its treatment were all six years ago. Other than the daily routine with the bag, I rarely think about it. Just occasionally if the subject comes up, or if I hear or read something, I think maybe this was more serious than I gave it credit for, but it's difficult to feel it's that important if you're not in pain and things are working. I had a hip replacement a year ago and now my knees are giving me far more pain than I ever had from my bladder. I am not a fan of statistics, because you can apply them in different ways depending on how you're feeling. The only statistic that did stay with me was that there was a good chance the cancer might come back within five years if I had radiotherapy. As my cancer had not got outside the bladder, it seemed a good opportunity to take it away and keep it that way. An emotional decision, I suppose, but it was informed by my reaction to the information I was given.

In some ways it has all seemed so easy. I felt very bad when my father died over twenty years ago, but the only time I feel I have suffered was later when my mother died, because I felt as if I had lost both of them, together, at that time. I have sometimes expected to feel more about the cancer, but that has never come. Working in the police service, I had a very active and, at times, unnerving career: my choices took me into some very nasty situations. I have been hurt and injured and in hospital as result, and I know I can cope. On many occasions in my work I was in danger of my life, but I have never felt that because of surgery, or having had cancer.

Chemo and cream cakes

Sarah was very apprehensive about having chemotherapy, but accepted that it was a necessary part of her treatment.

IN THE CHEMOTHERAPY ROOM, there were six big, bright-red chairs. Once you got 'your' chair, you had a nurse who administered the chemotherapy. Waiting nervously for mine to get started, sitting with my husband and best friend for moral support, I managed to look round at my fellow patients – and had a huge surprise. The other patients, who were already getting their chemo, were sitting eating cream cakes! That was so bizarre. I thought that chemo was going to make me sick! I needed chemotherapy because my breast cancer was invasive and had involved one of the lymph nodes. I had been feeling nervous all the way to the hospital and the oncologist had given me a drug to help me relax which worked really well, but gave the others a good laugh.

Once I got all hooked up and the chemo started, I started to cry because I knew what the drugs were supposed to do: they were to kill cancer. I was only thirty-nine and I shouldn't have cancer at my age. Then when I saw the first two syringes, I froze. They were bright red and I knew that was the drug that would make my hair fall out.

When the chemo was in, the nurse asked me if I wanted to go and see the lady in the wig room. My husband and friend walked me to see her, with me pushing my drip stand up the ward. That felt odd. I was convinced that a wig might go flying off my head in a wind, so I never went back. After everything was finished we set off home, feeling not too bad, but when we got there, I felt so tired I went straight to bed and slept for two and a half hours. Waking up, I felt terribly sick so took some more anti-sickness tablets and went back to sleep. On the third day, I had to have an injection and twelve hours after that my fingers and back were going mad. Something to do with the effect on the bone marrow, I am told. By the sixth day, I managed to drag myself out of bed, went for some shopping and then relaxed back home.

Three weeks after the first chemo, when I was due for the next lot, I wrote 'Going to get on top of the sickness this time. I'm ready for you!' And, it was a lot easier! No problems at all. No sickness. I even had salt and vinegar crisps and a fabulous lolly ice. Three days later, I was not a happy bunny but, by the end of the week, I was helping a friend with some painting.

Round three I was fine, but when my veins hardened with the chemo, I had to have a Hickman line put in. That was a life-saver and made having the rest of the chemo a lot easier. Cycle four I struggled a bit, but was okay. Cycle five was fine, too. Then cycle six, the last one. Woo hoo!! Guess what? *I was sitting there eating cream cakes!*

When I went for the last chemo, I talked with a lady in the waiting room. She'd seen the bandana I was wearing and said, "Excuse me, can I ask you a question? I'm having my first chemo in two weeks and I'm really nervous about it." I told her I was on my last one and said, "Don't be nervous. You will be a bit anxious the first time because you don't know what to expect. I'm not going to say it's easy. The first one is tough, but once you know what to expect you can figure it out as each cycle goes along, and it gets much better. I'm sure you'll be absolutely fine."

The relief on her face was lovely to see, and I wished I had met someone to tell me that before I started. You're anxious because you hear all the awful stories and it's not that bad. The nurses and doctors can't prepare you for it; they can tell you about the cycles and the side effects and this, that and the other, but each person is different and they can't tell what will happen to you. The best person to talk to is someone who has had chemotherapy. Life hasn't been all cream cakes, but that was a great feeling.

Decisions, decisions

*Roger was a town planner for many years, before moving to senior management
in the voluntary sector. Persuaded by a friend to train as a lay reader in the
Anglican church, he discovered he had prostate cancer a few weeks
after being ordained as an Anglican priest.*

WE HAD A DECISION TO MAKE: the PSA blood test was not normal. Although not very high, it was raised sufficiently (at a level of about seven) to suggest possible prostate cancer. Would we ignore it? Would we wait and see if it went higher? Or would I have a biopsy? Prostate biopsy was not without its risks, so we decided to wait a few months. I had been to the doctor four years before because of mild bladder symptoms and, on that occasion, the PSA test (Prostate Specific Antigen) had been normal. Alas, now, when it was repeated, the result was still abnormal. Given that there had been a lot of cancer in both our families this was not as frightening as it could have been. My wife had had breast cancer and her attitude was to get it sorted and to get it out of the way. We needed more information. Biopsies were taken, all of which showed prostate cancer.

I tend not to live in the here and now, but look to the future. Also, at sixty-three, I had just been ordained as a priest and our opinion was that God would not have gone to all that trouble for me just to die. We were both very optimistic and concentrated on the next decision: what treatment should I have? The cancer had not spread elsewhere and appeared to be confined to the prostate gland, so the choice was between radiotherapy and surgery, a radical prostatectomy. We had separate discussions with the surgeon and the radiotherapist before setting out on a cycling holiday from Zeebrugge to Brussels. Weighing up the pros and cons and considering the different side effects – possible damage to the bowel by radiotherapy, possible impotence or incontinence after surgery – reaching a decision was not easy. The deciding factor was my concern that after radiotherapy the prostate would still be there, and, as a medical friend commented, "It's better out and in the bin." Enjoying a break from cycling by a Belgian canal, I telephoned the cancer nurse specialist to report our decision.

The operation was straightforward and the PSA fell to the expected level which was fine, but I had more urinary incontinence than I had anticipated. I was dry at night quite quickly, but after several months I was still needing to use four or five incontinence pads during the day. Cycling was not a problem, no leakage at all, but I had to be careful when we stopped. Four years later, I had to be careful to change pads regularly, especially as control in the evenings was not good and if we went walking in the hills for more than an hour, it could be tricky finding a tree to change behind.

About eighteen months ago, the routine PSA test result showed a slight increase which was unsettling as it suggested there might still be a few cancer cells somewhere. Based on recent research, we were advised that if the PSA continued to rise, radiotherapy would be required to the area where the prostate had been and would be most effective before the PSA reached 0.5. As before, our approach was that if something needed to be done we would get on with it and I received four weeks of radiotherapy following which, the PSA fell to reassuring levels once again. Along with most other men who have had prostate cancer, for the past year I have continued to have regular PSA checks and, although I have been very matter-of-fact about it, I do get worried before the test. After the surgery, I was very confident that the cancer had been sorted, but then the PSA went up and I needed radiotherapy. I know several men with PSA levels far higher than mine and they are fine, and I know that if the PSA goes up yet again there is always hormone therapy and chemotherapy available, but I would be keen to avoid these if possible.

So far as the incontinence is concerned, I am well aware that there are many men who have had the same operation for prostate cancer who have had no problems at all and there are others whose life has been very restricted as a result. Recently, I had an operation that we hope will deal with the incontinence. Some men have an artificial urinary sphincter inserted, which has a high success rate, but there is also a more simple operation that uses a sling to prevent the leakage and there is an ongoing trial that compares the two. I volunteered for the trial and had a sling inserted several weeks ago. Although it is a relatively simple procedure, the post-operative discomfort has been considerable – even sitting at the computer has been tricky and I will not be mounting my bike for a quite a while yet! However, so far I have been substantially dry, with only slight leakage when I cough or sneeze, which is wonderful. If this is maintained, a major downside to the prostatectomy will have been dealt with.

Impotence (or erectile dysfunction as it is now called) was the other unwanted outcome of the radical prostatectomy. When it was clear that things were not going to return to normal, we were invited to meet with a nurse specialist who was able to explain the various treatment possibilities. She was very understanding, practical and thorough and it was helpful to know what was available and what might circumvent the problem. However, we had already discovered that intimacy could still be enjoyable despite the effects of surgery and decided not to try any of the treatments on offer. On the other hand we can, of course, change our minds at any time in the future if we wish.

Thinking back to our decision to choose surgery rather than radiotherapy, if I had known for definite that I would have been impotent and incontinent, I would certainly have been more hesitant, but it's impossible to know if we would have chosen differently. When my first wife died of cancer, I was very angry indeed, but I have not been angry at having cancer myself. In terms of my approach to life, cancer has brought home to me that we do not go on forever and that we do age. There are some things that can be put off, but if there are things we want to do, it's best to get on and do them.

Treating my prostate cancer has required a series of decisions which have been a challenge to deal with. First, having had the PSA test, there was the question about having a biopsy or not. After that, when it was clear I had cancer, there was the choice about treatment: surgery or radiotherapy. Following that, there was not only the disappointment with the incontinence and impotence, but a decision whether to have radiotherapy straight away when the PSA started to rise, or wait and see how it changed. Finally, there was a choice between two very different operations for the incontinence, by which time I was happy to leave the choice to a clinical trial. In facing these choices, there's no doubt that my wife's experience of breast cancer has helped both of us in dealing with my prostate cancer.

Self-help in the kitchen

When cancer surgery removed most of her stomach, Lynne found her own solution for her dietary problems.

BEFORE I COULD GO HOME, I had to eat, but I didn't feel hungry. I couldn't face the porridge they offered, the so-called scrambled egg was worse and the thick fortified drinks were undrinkable. Eventually, I managed a little soup and ice cream, then mince and mashed potato, but the hospital made no attempt to provide small, palatable meals suitable for someone who had just lost most of their stomach, even though my surgery had been done in their specialist gastric surgery unit.

My operation was a 'partial gastrectomy', which didn't sound too bad; they explained all about it, but I didn't take any of the details in. You just want it over and done with; you're concentrating on recovering and getting on with life again, not losing your stomach and gall bladder. When I learned afterwards they had taken four-fifths of the stomach away, that was a bit of a shock: there wasn't much left, was there? However, the cancer was gone and that was the most important thing. Even if I had known how it would affect my life, I would still have had it done.

The dietician was not a great help. She explained that I needed to put weight on and should eat high calorie food: milky coffee, cream cakes and the like, but I was worried about the fats and the cholesterol in these and, with my gall bladder gone as well, eating this sort of food made me feel awful. Once I was back at home, I was able to cook very small amounts of fresh food that suited me. My son was a great help with this because he's vegetarian and thinks a lot about his diet, and together we worked out small, balanced meals that were easy to eat, but still had the nutrition I needed.

One thing that nobody explains is that, in my situation, you have to concentrate on chewing all the time when you are eating. If you're talking and enjoying the conversation, it's easy to forget to chew thoroughly and then you pay for it later when the small stomach can't cope. I looked on the internet, but couldn't find a good forum about partial gastrectomy and although the Macmillan booklet was helpful, there isn't any of the sort of practical information you need, especially after stomach cancer. The hospital staff probably talked a bit about diet before the operation, but I really did not expect that food and eating would become such an issue for me.

Two months after leaving hospital, I saw the surgeon again and he thought I would not need any more treatment. My son came home at the weekend with flowers and champagne! He expected me to be over the moon with this news, but I wasn't so sure. Yes, it was good news, but how could I be sure there weren't some stray cancer cells floating about somewhere? I also knew that my results would be discussed by the multidisciplinary team, but I had not heard the outcome so I still felt in limbo. I should have been elated, but I wasn't. In the event, it was decided that chemotherapy would be advisable after all.

After the surgery and chemo, I had lost a lot of weight and then back at work, I lost even more. The reason for that was simple: with long journeys on public transport and then sitting at my desk at work, it was impossible to prepare and eat the small, homemade meals that I depended upon. I couldn't just eat a snack, or a sandwich, from the shop and my colleagues at work could not understand that. I had bought the Royal Marsden Hospital cook book and was already making the recipe for chocolate 'powerballs', but they, alone, were not the answer. The cook book is good for people on chemotherapy, but even their meals for one person did not solve my partial gastrectomy problem. When I lost more weight, the doctor was very clear: I would have to stop work. Something had to be done.

Thinking about the Royal Marsden chocolate balls gave me the idea that perhaps I could make the equivalent of an energy bar with different contents, that would include vitamins and have a variety of flavours, something more nutritious, that would be the right small size for someone with a very small capacity stomach – not just providing energy, but a little bit of everything that would contribute to a day's nutritional needs. Using some tips from my son, and experimenting with several on-line recipes, I now have a product that solves the problem. They are convenient, the right size, tasty (even for taste buds upset by chemotherapy), easy to eat, swallow and digest, and can be eaten between normal meal times without dampening the appetite. I started making them for myself, but other people have tried and liked them, so I've started a small business and have received orders from local shops. It seems they could also be good for people on chemotherapy, or people who have swallowing problems after treatment for oesophagus or head and neck cancer.

I call them 'Thrives Atoms'. If I had had these after surgery, my recovery would have been so much easier. Certainly, developing them has given me a focus and the confidence to do something for myself to help my own recovery. And if they can help other people recover from their cancer and its treatment, that would be wonderful.

Give my best to Doctor Roberts

The retired surgeon called into the local supermarket for some late shopping.
Turning the corner past the fruit and veg, he saw two men in their forties
deciding what to buy for their evening meal. One looked vaguely familiar.

"YOU'RE MISTER 'ALL," said a voice from behind. Turning round, the man he thought he recognised was extending a hand in greeting. "Yes. You're definitely Mister 'all, but you won't remember me. It's been a long time." Without waiting for any acknowledgement he turned to his friend.

"You remember when I had the cancer in me testicle that I told you about? Well, this is the bloke who cut off me ball. He then persuaded his mate, Doctor Roberts, to poison me with chemotherapy for six months. Bloody awful it was, but I survived. After that, he slit me open from top to bottom and cut out all me lymph nodes. Between the pair of them, they nearly killed me. But that was twenty years ago and here we are shopping for our supper."

With a final handshake and a broad grin they headed for the checkout. "Oh, don't forget to give my best to Doctor Roberts!"

I am privileged to be here

John was only seventeen and a devoted fan of the 1970s space-rock band Hawkwind when he was diagnosed with Hodgkin lymphoma. Here, he recounts how the music of an iconic rock band got him through.

IN 1975, I WAS A VERY IMMATURE, private, naïve seventeen-year-old who had wasted my time at school preferring to follow the rock band Hawkwind with a passion. I loved the escapism of the band, their lyrics about outer space, and followed them all over the country as often as I could afford. I wanted to follow my father as a plumber in the shipyards, but because I had played the practical joker at school and didn't study, I left with only a handful of worthless qualifications and had to settle for an apprenticeship in welding.

After a few months, I became increasingly fatigued, started losing weight, developed small breasts and even fell asleep at work at the bottom of a ship. The doctor put all this down to my teenage lifestyle, even depression, and then appendicitis, but eventually I was admitted to hospital for investigations.

Chemotherapy for Hodgkin lymphoma in the 1970s was very different from the treatment available now. The side effects were ghastly but, worse still, my emotions were all over the place. I was terrified by the prospect of dying. I was angry that I had not been told the truth. I was optimistic because I had so much to live for, not least my passion for Hawkwind, but inside I knew I might not survive. I was grateful that it was me and not my younger sister, but later I became suicidal. I couldn't talk with my parents, partly because I wanted to protect them; my sister was only thirteen and my mates had deserted me. I had so many questions, but often thought best not to ask them in case I didn't like the answer, an inherent fear of confronting my own mortality.

Treatment might have been doing me some good, but I had missed two gigs with Hawkwind, I was missing out on the money I needed from work, and I was missing life with my friends; I couldn't bring myself to be angry with my parents because they were finding it hard too, so I was angry with the chemo. After four cycles, I had had enough and decided not to go back. I convinced myself that the cancer had gone. Without telling anybody, I went back to work and forgot about the chemo.

A few weeks later there was a loud knocking at the door and there was the GP, the doctor who got my diagnosis wrong. Here he was, giving me a tirade about completing the chemotherapy, or else I would be arranging my own funeral. How dare he? I was furious! We exchanged loud words and I shut the door. Mum asked what was happening, so I explained, but that made her upset, and I was upset and did the usual thing – I went to my room, shut the door and listened to Hawkwind.

That night, I tossed and turned and probably matured faster than ever before, or since. I knew I had let myself down, I had let my parents down and the GP wouldn't have spoken as he did if he didn't have my best interests at heart. So, I went back to finish the chemo. But it hadn't worked. When I returned for the last cycle, the oncologist came and sat on the side of my bed, touched my hand and spoke to me for the very first time as an adult. The blood tests had shown that the cancer had not been controlled. I would need different chemotherapy.

Arrangements were made for the shipyard nurse to give me twice weekly injections. By comparison with the chemotherapy I had before, the side effects weren't bad and I managed to work and follow Hawkwind at their gigs. After that, I was 'in remission' and just needed follow-up at the hospital. They said I could return to 'normal life', but it wasn't exactly normal and I was not happy. I had missed out on teenage life and even now, my mates were protecting me; if there was a fight, they kept me out of it and I felt resentful. Then, just a few weeks later, the symptoms started again and the lumps came back. I had relapsed.

Chemotherapy started again, for the third time. It was my only chance, but after two cycles out of six, I was not coping. Fortunately, a young staff nurse helped me through and, once again, I was in remission. Or so we thought. In November 1976, the lumps came back. Three different combinations of chemotherapy had not been successful and there was no point in trying any more. However, there was an alternative that might be worth trying: radiotherapy. My situation was unusual and would need rather more radiation than usual. After twenty-five treatments to the centre of my chest, plus a single dose to the top half of the body, my 'get up and go' got up and left. I was exhausted and, at times, suicidal. My parents were fearful and celebrated Christmas early; antidepressants helped and getting back to work as soon as I was able restored some normality.

Easter came, but instead of Easter eggs, I got some new lumps in places they had not been before: I knew what that meant. Was this going to be it? Back at the clinic, they offered one possibility: a single chemotherapy drug used on its own in an experimental way. While I was receiving the first injection, my parents, in another room with the consultant, were being told that this fourth relapse would not be curable and treatment could only be palliative. Had I been told that so explicitly, I wonder if I would have returned for any more. We'll never know, but I do sometimes wonder.

When it was all finished, the outcome was assessed by a variety of blood tests and x-rays – CT and MRI scans were not available then – and I waited for days and long nights at home for the results. Once again, it was the magical universe of Hawkwind that carried me through the darkest hours. I thought that if the news was good, I might receive a phone call, but it never came and I was convinced the last chemo had failed as well. The following week, fearing the worst, I returned to the hospital. Walking along the corridor towards the clinic waiting room a door opened and the specialist stood before me. Raising his arms in triumph he shouted, "You're clear, all bloody clear!" and we shook hands. Words that I will never forget until the day I die, spoken forty years ago. And a doctor I will never forget, so humble and so caring.

Looking back those forty years, the treatment of cancer has changed, but what has not changed is the psychological burden, the fear factor, which goes hand in hand with the diagnosis of cancer. Treatment has changed, but people have not. Nobody has been able to explain how, or why, my cancer was cured and now, when I meet someone with a cancer that is probably not curable, I experience a strong feeling of guilt. I have survived, but they may not and I am reminded that often we are still impotent.

There have been consequences from my treatment. My pituitary gland has been suppressed by the salubrious chemotherapy and radiotherapy, so I need testosterone and thyroid hormone replacement. My lungs are scarred from the chemotherapy and radiotherapy resulting in occasional breathlessness and the need for inhalers, and I have needed a skin cancer to be removed that was caused by the treatment. All of that said, I do feel that life is so sweet. I am privileged to be here.

Remission is a funny word

To Do List

Go to tip
Nick-nacks to car boot sale.
Crockery to charity shop.
Books to hospital
Clothes to hospice
Up-date will

Robert Alley
2016

A S WE SET OFF FOR THE HOSPITAL, I looked back thinking I might not see my home and lovely garden again. Strangely, it did not really bother me. I was not frightened of being dead. When the consultant had said there were two small tumours in my lungs, I thought straight away that it was lung cancer and had decided that would not be good.

Once in hospital, investigations revealed the true diagnosis: non-Hodgkin lymphoma. "Is that good?" I asked.

"Well, we can treat it, but you'll need several months of chemotherapy."

By this time, I had already lost three stone in weight and had needed a couple of blood transfusions. In hospital, I needed a wheelchair even to have a simple x-ray. The whole thing had sneaked up on me, and on the doctors, too. Now that I am better and can walk upstairs it's a real pleasure.

When I finished the first three cycles of chemotherapy the oncologist showed me the scan and explained that the tumours, in my neck, chest and abdomen, had shrunk miraculously from over nine centimetres to less than two centimetres. A very welcome result.

Through all of this, we had never talked about my prognosis and the first time it dawned on me was when the nurse gave me the 'red book', the patient-held chemotherapy record that everyone is given to keep track of their treatment. I was so tired I hadn't actually asked anybody about my likely prognosis, but where, at the beginning of the book, it says 'Reason for Treatment' and I read 'Curative' I thought, 'Ah, that's all right then'. I had had tumours in my bladder and breast cancer eight years before and because of this, in some ways, I was quite blasé about this one, but it was encouraging to see that they thought I could be cured.

After six cycles, I was told that the scans were clear: I was 'in complete remission'. But that's a funny word. In his letter to my doctor, the specialist wrote, "She is in complete remission and I could not be happier." Unfortunately, I could not feel as happy. I know the oncologists cannot say that you're cured, but 'in remission' leaves the feeling that perhaps the cancer is just sleeping somewhere. It's a difficult word; it doesn't give you the feeling that the problem has been sorted.

It was at this point that the oncologist suggested I could have some radiotherapy, to complete the treatment. At first I thought I should agree because everybody had been so helpful, it might add something to the so-called remission and it would be wrong not to take advantage of all treatment available. I had had radiotherapy for breast cancer in the past, so I knew it wasn't bad, however, the prospect of travelling for daily treatment for three weeks, just as I was beginning to get my life back, was not attractive. Also, this was the third time I had developed cancer and if I really was cured of the lymphoma, I might need radiotherapy in the future for another cancer and I knew you couldn't have radiotherapy to the same place more than once. I needed to know much more about the benefit of the proposed radiotherapy before making a decision. The answer was that it would reduce the chance of the lymphoma coming back by two-and-a-half percent. Was that all? Two-and-a-half percent? Well, it just wasn't worth all the hassle and the possible implications for the future. If it had been twenty percent, I might have thought differently, but for such little benefit, I decided 'no thank you'.

Back at home, after I had finished chemotherapy, I was able to do more and my hair was starting to grow, but I could not make plans. Friends wanted to arrange a celebratory lunch, but I didn't have the confidence to plan even a few weeks ahead. I was on my own again, friends were visiting less and I should have been feeling much better, but I was panicking. I suppose that having been preoccupied with all the treatment and finding myself on my own again I was back to my first feelings, facing my mortality, and needing to get the house sorted. To anyone who asked, I was fine, and I was fine physically, but inside I was still anxious. Nobody had ever given me any idea that I might feel like that and as a result I felt guilty: everybody had done so much, the hospital had worked wonders, the specialist was pleased, the family were delighted, but I was still feeling sorry for myself. Fortunately, an urgent appointment with an understanding doctor and some mild antidepressants were helpful. Even more so was seeing a counsellor, which surprised me.

Before I was ill, I had not really thought about the future. I had enjoyed a very good life, forty years of happy marriage and a busy and merry widowhood. I have been very lucky, but, with the lymphoma 'in remission', I was forced to face the possibility that I might lose my independence and might become a burden on my family. Knowing what had happened to my brother and my husband as they died, I was worried by that and thought I would rather be dead, but for that to happen, I needed to be organised and leave nothing for the family to clear up after me. After all, I am the matriarch of the family! If the doctors are right, that's probably not going to be necessary for a long time yet, but believing them, and getting one's confidence back, is a different matter.

After I had breast cancer, I was 'in remission', but the cancer had been cut out; there had been a bad bit and it was gone. This time, the lymphoma has just disappeared and that is not so convincing. My confidence is improving now and I've booked to attend a conference in two months' time, although I had to pay the full price for the hotel room as I am not sufficiently confident that I may not need to cancel at the last moment. On the other hand, I have had the car serviced and am looking forward to using it to visit distant friends who I have not seen for far too long.

Things started looking up

LIFE HAD BEEN PRETTY GOOD up to this point, but after repeated requests by my partner to 'get it seen to', that was about to change. I had been experiencing difficulty in relieving myself and going to the toilet repeatedly. Of course, I had ignored the problem; I always thought it didn't matter. After thirty years in secondary education, I had plenty of other things still to do. I had just retired and was looking forward to new adventures in life. It seemed that would all change when prostate cancer was diagnosed.

The recommended treatment was to include seven weeks of radiotherapy along with three years of trimonthly injections of hormone pellets, apparently the full dose available to any one individual. The consultant thought a young, fit lad like me could handle it. Initial tablets and injections prepared the way for the radiotherapy and small tattoos aided the direction of the radiotherapy beam when I was moved slowly in the gigantic oval machine. I was offered the option of taking music to listen to but, as the idea was to remain still and not move, I thought that the Rolling Stones 'Route 66' would not be a good choice!

At first, my visits were not difficult and, with some humour thrown in by the radiographers, things progressed nicely. As the weeks progressed, the side effects which I had been warned about became quite acute: the phrase 'I didn't know whether I wanted a shit or a haircut' came to mind. In the last two weeks, it was necessary to take somebody with me for support and during the last week, when I couldn't trust myself on public transport, my youngest daughter took time off work to take me by car. I was to find out later that my symptoms had ranked quite high in the great scheme of things. Most men don't seem to suffer as much as I did after radiotherapy, and some none at all. Lucky lads. This turned out to be the most trying time, but it was manageable. I was assured that the symptoms would subside after a few months and, eventually, they did.

Over the ensuing three years of hormone treatment, my PSA levels came down. Prostate Specific Antigen is a blood test that indicates activity of the prostate cancer, so I was always relieved when, prior to the hormone pellet injection, I was informed that the latest blood test showed that it was still down. I must admit, I still had worrying thoughts about the hormone treatment. It was supposed to lessen the effects of testosterone, which apparently fed the cancer, so what would happen when the treatment finished? These things did focus my mind even more than before. Intimacy had taken a severe bashing as well; the hormone treatment lessened one's libido, but I'm pleased to say that after three long years things are starting to look up, if you get my drift. Life expectancy levels had been published from medical surveys and being a pragmatic kind of guy, I gave myself ten good years to live and decided to make the most of it. If my life continued further, that would be a bonus.

Life goes on, a new normal life, not as before, obviously, but I have been determined to stay as positive as possible; I continue walking with friends, playing tennis and keeping active. Also, travelling the world has become more important to me because I had become acutely aware that there was a big, wide world out there that I hadn't seen. So, last year it was Australia and this year it was six great weeks in India and Nepal. Friends often say how well I am looking. Yes, I do, but this was down to hard work and effort!

Work was out of the question

Stan worked as a long-distance lorry driver. Aged fifty-six,
prostate cancer was diagnosed.

THE HARDEST THING I FOUND was making the appointment to see the doctor in the first place. For three or four years, I was getting up far too often in the night, having problems with erections, saw adverts on television that struck home and was elbowed in the ribs by my brother, who had prostate cancer, to 'get it sorted out'.

I didn't think it would be cancer for me, but the doctor said, "You've asked for a PSA test, so that's what we'll do." The PSA (prostate specific antigen) was 103 which, in the doctor's opinion, meant I had cancer. That was hard to take. My wife and I were devastated. When I was a child, cancer meant you were going to die and that thought would not go away.

Up to the hospital for biopsies and other tests. Although my brother had been through the process, all he would say was, "Go with the flow, don't resist and you'll be all right." Not painful, just strange, intrusive, embarrassing, cold, clinical, in a small room with no windows, no clothes, a far too small gown, no empathy, waiting for a doctor who had been delayed. I was frightened and about to walk out, but then he walked in. After that, I just survived the unbelievable noise of the MRI scan and then fell asleep for the bone scan! Then back for the results. They've got to tell you, but there are ways of doing it and mine was not good. It seemed I couldn't be cured, but I would give it a good go and hope the treatment could do something. I started the hormone tablets straight away and the first injection followed three weeks later.

All this time I continued to work, but found I started to make mistakes. Physically, I was fine and could work, but knowing that I had cancer and then being told that I may have only months to live, I could not concentrate and became unreliable. I was a heavy-goods driver and although I'd chucked in the long distance work, I was an emergency driver between the docks and a car manufacturer. If they needed bolts, they needed them in twenty minutes and if I was slow, or took them to the wrong depot, the production line was held up. The thought of the company losing £17,000 a minute because of me not getting bolts to the right place quickly enough was a bit much. The three weeks of tablets were all right, but when the injections started they finished me: the side effects and the lethargy started within a few days, and the mood swings were something I had never experienced before. The tiredness just suddenly overtakes you, so I wasn't safe to drive. I could easily fall asleep at the wheel and end up killing somebody, or killing myself. Work was out of the question.

Eighteen months later, I still get the hot flushes, the tiredness and the mood swings, but not as much. It's not great, but there isn't any choice and so long as my PSA keeps coming down, I'm happy. It's been a bit of a journey, but other people's journeys have been far worse than mine. If I could work, I would, but that's not possible because I would be a danger to the public. Retraining for something else takes concentration and I simply haven't got it. As soon as they can stop the injections, I'll be back to work. Medically, I haven't suffered much; apart from the shock at the beginning and the side effects of the hormones, it hasn't been bad – being stabbed by the nurse every three months is no big deal. I really feel for those who have to go through the medical hoop; I've had it easy so far.

What shall I tell the Missus?

IT HAD BEEN A BUSY MORNING and the surgeon thought his prostate cancer clinic had finished. Just as he was leaving, Sister called him back. "There's an elderly man still sitting in the waiting area who is reluctant to leave. I'm sure he was the first one here this morning. Could you have a word with him?"

He was, indeed, the first patient of the day with whom the surgeon had spent a long time talking about his diagnosis of prostate cancer and the treatment he would need. He had seemed satisfied with the information he had been given, appeared to understand what the treatment would involve, had a prescription in his hand and had been booked an appointment for the scan he would need before starting his tablets. What was keeping him?

"You explained all about the cancer and I think I understand what the treatment will be like, and I'm not bothered by that. But when I was waiting for the bus to go home another thought struck me and I didn't know what to do. The question is, what shall I tell the Missus? I mustn't upset her."

Clearly the clinic had not finished, but twenty minutes later, the gentleman stood to leave. "Thank you. I think I've worked out what to say now." As he left for the bus a second time, he even managed a hesitant smile for Sister and promised to bring 'The Missus' with him next time.

Just the two of us

At forty-four years of age, Louise was still hoping to get pregnant. She knew it was getting late, but there could be a last chance; she could still hope. Then cancer was diagnosed and the treatment would require a radical hysterectomy. Not only was there the devastating fact of cancer to face, all her final hopes evaporated in that moment when she was told what the treatment would entail. She would never be able to conceive or carry a baby. It would be 'just the two of us'. In addition to the 'C' word, it was the 'H' word that took its toll. To try and understand what she was feeling, and to come to terms with what lay ahead, Louise wrote her thoughts and feelings down. Somehow, seeing them on paper, in black and white, made them easier to face. She then sent them, as a letter to her husband in the hope that they would help him understand, too. They had written notes to each other before, but now it took on quite a different significance, and the healing process started.

Before Cancer: I love, fancy, admire and respect you. You are my friend first and foremost, my hubby and the person I choose to share my life with.

After Cancer: You are my hubby and the person I choose to share my life with. You are also my soulmate whether we are married or not. I love you for being you. I love sharing my life with you, however long that might be.

Before: We will be there for each other, no matter what.

After: Cancer is ultimately a very lonely experience and there are times when I know you don't understand why I still get upset about everything that's happened, even though it's been quite a few months since being given the all clear. I'm actually glad you don't fully understand what it's been like for me. I never want you to know what it's like to receive a shock cancer diagnosis and then have to lose parts of your body that you never want to lose. That loss feels unbearably sad for me at times, but I know that you love me even when I'm low and I couldn't have got through this in the same way without you.

Before: I never thought about having a baby until I met you. After we got married, I wanted to get pregnant very, very much. By you and only ever you. It never happened though and although we were accepting of that, we never thought that cancer would take away any last chance of a 'what if …'

After: I sometimes wonder what it would have been like if we'd had a daughter. I'm guessing, for you, that Alex would have been a boy! Either way, I think we would have made good parents. Anyway, I'm not going to cry any more about 'what if', but I hope you understand that I've needed to do this in order to move through my own personal loss. It's going to be just the two of us (well, us and a very cute cat) and thankfully we're both OK with that. Family can mean whatever we want it to mean and as long as there is love for ourselves and others, we can be a family in many different ways.

Before: I never thought I'd be diagnosed with cervical cancer. I went for all my smears, never missed one, had no symptoms and had always received normal results until 2014. Receiving my first abnormal screening letter was scary enough in itself and even the colposcopy nurse reassured us, until she took one look down below. The room went silent. I actually felt that time stopped during that traumatic moment.

I then became distraught and you were brought into the room. It was especially hard when no one knew what to say or do after I broke down in tears asking WHY? But you never left my side. Oh, and why did this have to happen on our wedding anniversary? Cancer really doesn't care about anyone, or anything, does it?

After: Errors happen and we now know that an error happened to me. Sadly, my case has become another false negative statistic. My previous screening was incorrectly reported as normal when, in fact, it showed abnormalities and we now know I was left untreated for three years. The impact of that error, and how it has been handled, has been truly devastating. Even so, I am still extremely thankful to the cervical screening programme and for the existence of all other cancer screening programmes. That is why I continue to fully support them and encourage my family and friends to attend their appointments. *Please!*

Before: Neither of us had any major health concerns and we bounce back quickly from any illnesses.

After: This has floored me physically and emotionally. I know you think it's taking me far longer to 'recover' than you ever expected, but I simply cannot bounce back this time. However, I'm also under no illusions that in the gynae-oncology world, a radical hysterectomy with no further adjuvant treatment is considered a highly desired and favourable outcome. However, in my world, it still feels overall a pretty crap situation to be in, especially when we're at the follow-up appointments. They are such a big reminder about everything that's happened. You always come with me, though, and I cannot even begin to tell you how much I appreciate that. Thank you, my love. It does occur to me that although the professionals may treat us in an efficient and caring way, the treatment felt like being on a conveyor belt and it seems to me that they really have little, or even no, idea of the impact that their work has on their patient.

Before: Despite being self-conscious about being a bit pear-shaped, I loved sharing my body with you.

After: I feel different about sharing now. Cancer developed in a very intimate area of my body and I still find it hard, at times, to block this out. This is what I mean when I say I feel assaulted by cancer. I am trying my best to accept and like what is left behind now that the assault is over. You tell me that you still love my body and that helps. A lot.

94

Before: I experienced deep and intense sexual satisfaction with you on a very regular basis.

After: Since the hysterectomy, my body's responses are not as spontaneous or as intense now, but the emotional intimacy I feel for you is through the roof. I love my body and I love yours and feel very connected to you at a deep level when we're together. It's taken quite a while, but sex is finally starting to feel good again. Reading that Macmillan book was really helpful.*

Before: I took how our bodies worked, and its functions, for granted and didn't give many things a second thought.

After: I appreciate our bodies so much more than before. When I was told that my bladder function would probably be affected by the surgery, the thought of not being able to wee properly upset me out of all proportion. I could tell how proud you were when I told you about being able to go to the loo successfully after the catheter was first removed. After nine years of marriage, we now really understand the true meaning of 'in sickness and in health' … and in toilet habits!

Before: I thought the radical hysterectomy would be a simple operation because it was keyhole surgery.

After: It's not a simple operation at all. Even though I only have very small scars, it was major surgery and, combined with lymph node removal, it was a long and complex procedure. I was also surprised that post-surgical difficulties can continue for several months afterwards. I now have continual lower back pain, groin pain and ongoing numbness to the top of my legs, but things are slowly getting better. I may have been able to drive six weeks after the surgery, but the reality is that it can take a very long time to recover fully and some things are simply never the same again. Thank you for asking how I'm handling being on HRT; I thought that was very empathic of you. It's the fear of cancer returning that I struggle with the most, but we rarely talk about that. I understand why, though, and I really do embrace positivity. Most of the time.

* '*Sexuality and cancer for women.*' Published by and available from Macmillan Cancer Support.

Before: Uncertainty was not a word in my vocabulary!

After: Whilst hope and faith are a great help, and I really do believe that I'm going to be OK, I now live with an uncertainty that I've never had to consider before. I'm told that the tumour was removed completely during surgery, but I'm also told I'm not cured either because there's always a chance that the cancer might come back. For me, this feels like limbo, but I hope you know that I do feel very positive about the future. My future and our future.

Before: I was a bit bothered about getting older, growing older and looking older.

After: I'm not bothered whatsoever and the thought of ageing now seems such a beautiful and natural process. I really want to get old. With you.

Before: Although I knew that death happens and we have both been bereaved in the past, my death was an abstract concept until it actually came to having to face the possibility of dying.

After: Because no one could tell us initially whether the cancer was at an advanced stage or not, that early part of the process felt like a very, very long wait. I know that you (and pretty much everyone else) thought I was being overly pessimistic during that time, but I wasn't. I was actually trying to come to terms with the possibility of dying, my own death, and this in itself brought up a big dollop of death anxiety. Thankfully, having access to counselling felt like a life-line and I cannot thank those involved enough for their support. Thank you for encouraging me to go. By being able to talk about this, I no longer fear death in the same way that I did and I now value life and our togetherness even more. The possibility of dying also brought up a big dollop of love and I got a huge urge to tell everyone that means something to me that I love them. And I did just that. And I still do.

Before: I love you so much.

After: I still love you so much. Nowt changes there. You texted me when I was in hospital to tell me that I was your world. Well, you're my world, too. Sometimes, our world is just the two of us and that's just fine.

Help is at hand

THERE SEEMS TO BE A PROCESS when you're dealt bad news. At first there's the anger, 'Why me?' and all that, until you reach the acceptance. I still get the occasional why-me day: I'm only fifty-seven and want to live till I'm eighty, but it's not going to happen. The nurse suggested that it might be helpful if I saw a clinical psychologist. I was desperate for anything that might help and I'm pleased to say it was reasonably successful: she set my brain in the right direction. At first, I saw her every week, then once a fortnight, then once a month and after six months we finished, and I haven't needed to see her again. I think the psychologist led me through the thought process minefield of what's important and what's not important, what you can push to one side and what has to be done now. I was trying to deal with everything all at once, so my head was going round like a kaleidoscope and I couldn't slow it down enough to put things in the right pigeon holes. Eventually, it did slow down and everything fell into place, and now we've got some order back in life. It's no good to keep asking the same question over and over, because you know the answer! One day you wake up and the light goes on in your head: I've got it and I've got to deal with it.

IF I TRIED QUESTIONING the nursing or medical staff, no honest answers were forthcoming; I couldn't talk with my parents, partly because I wanted to protect them; my sister was only thirteen and my mates had deserted me. I had so many questions, but often thought best not to ask them in case I didn't like the answer, an inherent fear of confronting my own mortality. It was only by talking through the night with other patients, fellow cancer sufferers in the ward, that I found some help. When I returned later for chemotherapy, renewing some of these friendships helped me to survive the side effects – and to cope with my anger at the treatment.

WHEN I WENT IN TO SEE THE ONCOLOGIST, we asked him all our questions, and he answered them. That was a game changer! Going home, we felt so much more positive. We had confidence that we understood what was happening, we would get honest answers to our questions, I could be confident for the future and the specialist team were concerned for me as a whole person. I cried once, but didn't cry again about the cancer.

HUNTING ON THE INTERNET is not necessarily a good idea, but I did speak with some American lads in chat rooms who had a similar diagnosis. From them I learned they had had their cancers quite a long time, like me, and what they said was, "You'll have a tough time to come in a few years." Years to come? Well, that was better than the months to come that I had been told by the medics, so I gained some comfort from them. That really was the first indication that it was not all doom and gloom. I probably won't be cured, but I'll give it a good go and hope the treatment they give me does something.

LUCKILY, MY MOTHER WAS VERY PROACTIVE. She went hunting on the internet to find anything that might explain what was happening to me and what could, or should, be done. Amazingly, she found 'Butterflies', a thyroid cancer telephone support charity, founded by Kate Farnell in Newcastle, a huge, huge help! Kate and her colleagues at Butterflies have all had thyroid cancer and know what it's like. We had no idea why I was feeling so awful, whether or not I would need more treatment, what that might be, anything: Kate was able to explain it all.

WHEN I WAS FIRST DIAGNOSED, I felt quite isolated because I didn't want to burden my family with the way I was feeling. I was putting on a brave face, but inside I was crumbling. One day at work, I saw the word 'cancer' on a notice board. I approached to have a closer look at the poster: it said 'Cancer Connections' which was, apparently, a local support group. When I walked through the door, I knew I had come to the right place. This was my escape where I was able to cry, be sad, talk and laugh. No judgements, just love all round. Most of the volunteers had gone through cancer, or knew someone who had experienced cancer, so they knew where I was coming from. My children started to attend with me, and my husband when he was not working, which made things so much easier for us all as a family.

WHEN I GLEANED MORE INFORMATION from the hospital about the aggressiveness of the cancer, that was the first step. My prostate cancer was a Gleason 9, with seminal vesicle invasion and some pelvic lymph nodes destroyed, bone scan clear. The Macmillan website was helpful, but I got near the bottom before I found my stage so I thought, 'Blimey, there's not far to go here before I fall off the edge!'

MY LITTLE GIRL, who is now five years old, also comes to see a counsellor who has been trained especially to help children. To a child, it is so hard to explain what is happening and she started having panic attacks when she was away from me. She had to watch her mummy go through an operation, chemotherapy and radiotherapy. She has had an awful lot to deal with in such a short time, but she turned it all round. She became the mammy! She was my rock, at four years old.

AT THE CANCER SUPPORT CENTRE, they welcomed me and my partner and when someone asked, "How are *you*?" that was when the volcano erupted: all my pent-up emotions just came bursting out. Here was someone who wanted to help and I could let it all out. I was in my own little world and I needed to release my feelings. It was like a relief valve. Luckily, there was a box of tissues. It was embarrassing, but I felt miles better.

THE COMPLEMENTARY THERAPISTS WERE LOVELY. They have the knack of bringing the best out of people and you could talk about anything with someone you didn't know while you were enjoying a massage. Whenever my wife had a therapy, she was lifted; she looked six feet tall. It did her the world of good and the benefit lasted for days. There may be some physical benefit from reflexology, I don't know, and I'm a sceptic, but the mental effect is huge. Being free to talk about anything and everything while it is happening is very therapeutic. Reiki is different: I don't speak a word, the mind floats off into the ether, there's a wonderful feeling of peace and contentment and I feel great for a day or two afterwards. It's impossible to describe and for an engineer and scientist like myself it's bunkum, but it is not.

The Professor

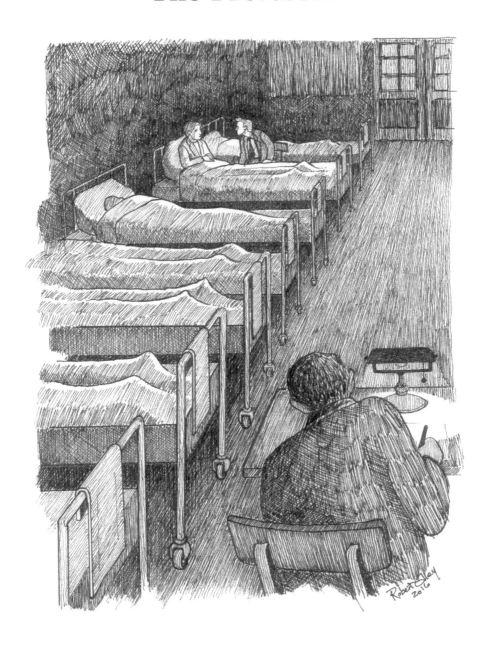

IT WAS LATE, nearly midnight. The newly qualified house surgeon was sitting at the desk in the middle of the darkened ward working by the light of the old-fashioned, green-shaded lamp. Hearing the door of the ward open, he looked up to see who might be coming in so late. Night Sister, tyrant of the wee small hours doing her rounds? An unexpected emergency admission? The night porter bringing the blood transfusion he was waiting for?

It was the Professor. Wearing his immaculate suit and perfect tie even at this late hour, he slipped in silently and went to the second bed on the right. Drawing up a chair, he spent the next half hour talking with the occupant, and then disappeared as quietly as he had come.

"What's the Prof doing here at this time of night?"

"No idea," replied Staff Nurse. "I've never seen him on the ward as late as this."

The following morning, waiting for the gentleman to be anaesthetised for his bowel cancer operation, the young doctor was still puzzled. "Excuse me, sir, I hope you do not mind my asking, but why did you come to the ward so late last night? Was there a problem?"

The Professor, senior surgeon in a London university hospital, explained that after the morning ward round, he realised that the man due for bowel cancer surgery was still very fearful and was convinced he was going to die. "As I was going to bed, this troubled me and I thought it might help if he and I talked about it again. That way, I had a good night's sleep and I hope he did too."

The operation was successful and the man made a quick recovery. Saying goodbye a few days later, the young doctor mentioned the incident. "He gave me the shock of me life when he came in like that; I thought something was up. But when he explained again about the cancer and what he was going to do I felt much better and managed to get to sleep. He's a decent chap that Professor of yours. He really understood."

102

Feelings

Professional, male and forty. Are you prepared to talk about your feelings?

MY FIRST CONTACT WITH CANCER was at school where I was a keen swimmer and a lifeguard. We were shown a video about cancer which focused on a man who could not swim because he had cancer in his larynx that had left him with a tracheotomy. That really stuck with me. Then, when I was twenty-one, a very good friend died of a brain tumour. After I visited his parents, I sat in the car and sobbed, overwhelmed with grief.

By my late thirties I was married, had a good job, nice house, had a child, lots of responsibility – everything was comfortable. As happens with us all, my grandfather died and I was there when he passed. Then six months later, at the age of sixty-three, my father was diagnosed with mesothelioma which could not be cured. My mam would not talk about it, but there was lots about mesothelioma in the news and on television, so my father could not avoid it and I had conversations with him trying to be tough and protect him. He also told us, his family, that everything was all right when it wasn't and at the end, when he was in hospital, I had to tell my mam and sister that he was dying and had only days to live. When he died, as a defence mechanism, I detached myself from it all.

During my dad's illness, my then wife became pregnant with our second child, which should have been a happy time, but I couldn't bond with the 'bump' that would turn into our gorgeous daughter. I was frightened something would go wrong and my feelings mirrored my father's feelings: he didn't want to be involved with a baby who he thought he would not see. After my daughter was born, he saw her only once and died a few weeks later. He just switched off and seeing her was too much for him.

As the son in the family, it fell to me to arrange the funeral and sort things out. Having built my defence mechanism, this was not difficult and I was happy to do it to protect those around me. At the funeral I felt nothing, no emotion whatsoever, looking at other people crying, but not wanting to cry myself. It was all a bit surreal. What was also happening, without me realising, was that I was pushing my family and friends away. I thought I was protecting them, but in reality I did not want them to know what I was feeling. I did not want to talk about feelings any more. I was happy to help anyone else and talk about how they were, but I did not want to talk about me.

After my mam died two years later, life was very busy: the children were growing and I had a busy job that involved lots of travel. Despite my 'defence mechanism', dealing with another loss in the family had not been easy. I loved my parents dearly, but at both funerals I felt no emotion. I do remember thinking at my mam's funeral that it was strange, but I just carried on. There was a close friend of my mother who seemed to understand what I was going through with whom I was able to talk, at least superficially, skimming round the edges, but she had breast cancer which recurred and she died.

Despite this, friends and family who were upset felt they could come to me with their problems because they thought I was okay. Outwardly, I looked fine and would do everything I could to help, but in reality, I was busying myself with other people's problems so that I did not have to sit down and look at my own. Inside, sometimes, I was screaming. I threw myself into my work and my children, but I was no longer sociable, colleagues noticed a change in me, and I had become detached from those around me. Eventually, I left the job that I enjoyed because I was unhappy and thought it was due to work. In reality, my mind was trying to grieve, but I wouldn't let it. In the months that followed, there were other deaths in the family and I didn't cry once. Finally, a cousin, younger than me, with whom I was able to talk, developed breast cancer and died leaving her husband with two young children.

Through all of this, people have asked me, were there no colleagues at work in whom I could confide? The answer is quite simple: No! Working in a big firm in a senior position, wanting to talk with a colleague about a personal problem like bereavement would have been seen as a sign of weakness. Take time off work 'with anxiety and depression', even to cope with a parent's death, and you could be out of a job. I knew that I could not talk to anybody at work and never tried.

The change in my emotions was highlighted one evening in a bar where I was enjoying a quiet drink. A guy I had met before came up and started being funny with his friends and I suspected it was going to end up in a confrontation. In the past, my reaction was always to leave and walk away – if it's fight or flight, I would chose flight! But that night, I stayed put and wasn't scared at all. If he wanted trouble, I remember thinking I would batter the guy and his mates; I just didn't care anymore. Nothing actually happened, but afterwards I realised that something had changed in me, and it wasn't right, but I wasn't going to give it any more thought. The only people my mind let me feel true emotion for were my two fantastic children; everyone else I was pushing away.

A few days later, at work in the office, I suddenly thought I was having a heart attack. Out of nowhere it felt as if my heart was beating out of my chest, I had chest pain and I was scared. I was on the verge of ringing 999 for an ambulance, but I went to a quiet office and, after ten minutes or so, managed to calm myself down, reckoning it had been an anxiety attack. It happened again when I was at home and over the next few months, they became frequent. I found that I could not sleep and I could not relax, even with the children; there was a tension all the time and I became argumentative and more solitary. Still not acknowledging my problem, I thought I would help a charity that had supported my cousin and her family, but instead, and to my surprise, my own need was recognised and counselling was offered. Today, I have no idea where I would be without the help that provided.

Has the counsellor fixed me? No, because I don't think one ever gets one hundred percent fixed. But looking at it a different way, could I have been on the long term sick?

Yes. Could I have become a burden? Yes, not a shadow of doubt. Could I have cared for my kids the way I have? No way. My advice to anyone in a similar situation? Please don't go through what I went through. If you are a bloke, suck it up and talk to somebody. It's not weakness, there's no stigma telling your loved ones you are struggling. Seek help. It's probably the best thing you can do.

Fear

DO NOT FEAR, FOR I AM WITH YOU. DO NOT BE DISMAYED, I AM YOUR GOD. I WILL STRENGTHEN YOU AND HELP YOU.

Robert Olley
2016

MY CHILDHOOD HAD BEEN HAPPY. I had married my school sweetheart and he was intelligent, handsome and successful. We had three lovely sons and a home by the sea. However, in the past my life had not been without its traumas. My mother had breast cancer when I was eleven years old, my auntie died of breast cancer when I was thirteen, and then my mum died in a car crash when I was twenty-nine, a few months before the birth of my third son. That pregnancy was perfect, but after the birth there were complications: I ended up in intensive care and was not expected to survive. Then, at forty-five, I divorced and found myself on my own. Despite all this, I had never experienced fear which, I think, was because of my very strong Christian faith.

Because of my mother's cancer at a young age, I had mammograms every year till I was fifty and then three-yearly after that. When I was fifty-four, it showed a lump that I could not feel, a cancer that had already spread under the arm.

The surgeon had been very encouraging and said he would come to see me after the operation, but he didn't, so I thought he hadn't come because he didn't want to tell me what he had found. When another doctor came, I asked how they could be sure the cancer hadn't spread. She said they couldn't. That hit me because they never talk like that in the clinic. They always keep it light and happy and say you'll be fine so you never worry. It never crossed my mind that it might have spread. The tumour was only two and a half centimetres and grade two, but when she said they couldn't be sure it hadn't spread I started worrying. When I got the results of the surgery and the cancer had gone to five lymph nodes, I worried even more. I had my promise from the Bible and knew that God would hold my hand, but that was when the fear set in.

Before the chemo started, my routine bone scan was not normal. The oncologist said there were 'hot spots', whatever they are. When she said that, to me it meant the cancer had spread to my bones. I felt like that little rabbit and could think of nothing else.

It was four days before Christmas. As we left, she said, "I'm sorry I have had to tell you this." I was terrified and convinced that would be my last Christmas. An MRI scan was done after Christmas and on the 4th January, I was told the bones were clear after all. That was all I wanted to hear! I didn't listen to anything else, but the oncologist was trying to say they had found something else. Although the cancer had not spread to the bones, the scan had shown something inside the spinal column at the top. The oncologist didn't think it was anything to do with the breast cancer, but it needed investigation. I would need to see a brain surgeon. At that time I wasn't really concerned by this, because all I wanted was to start the chemo for my breast.

When I did see the brain surgeon, that made the fear much worse. Although he agreed that the thing they could see on the MRI probably was not a metastasis from the breast cancer, he couldn't rule it out one hundred percent. It was probably something that had been there for years. But he couldn't guarantee it was not cancer. That frightened me. If you are the person with the cancer, whether it has come back or not is black or white, not maybe. The fear was incredible. Even though I had my faith and friends at the church who were helping me, I was frightened. I did not want to die. All those reassuring things I had read, and people were telling me, I couldn't hear.

In the middle of the radiotherapy, my twenty-two year old youngest son started to complain of double vision. On the last day of my radiotherapy, the eye specialist 'phoned to say that his scan had shown something in the brain stem, possibly a brain tumour, and a neurosurgeon would need to be involved. I had my last radiotherapy treatment that afternoon and then we had to concentrate on my son.

Tests were done that confirmed a brain tumour. Because of its position in the brain stem it could not be removed with surgery and he would have to go for radiotherapy urgently. The young oncologist we met was brilliant in the way she told him, but when he asked if he would survive she could not say whether he would have one year or five. I tried to help by reminding him we had faith, but he pushed me away and began to get angry and left the room. The doctor was upset by his reaction and thought she had explained the situation badly, but there was no way of giving that sort of news without a shock and she had been very kind. Also, she knew about my own recent treatment, so she called my oncologist and the three of us talked together. When the boys came back, they were much more cheerful with the friendly staff. The six weeks of radiotherapy that followed is over a year ago and my boy is well and back at work running his business.

When I first realised the seriousness of my son's brain tumour, I was devastated. When I shared the news with my best friend, she was angry, she even shouted that it was not fair for one person to have so much trouble. She has since been a wonderful help. People ask me, "How did you cope? How have you kept going?"

The first thing has been my faith and the support of so many people in the church, and holding on to that little promise from the Bible that I still carry with me every day. But even with my faith, I still needed help to deal with the fear. The fear was not knowing. When you get the thought that the cancer could still kill you, it's out of your hands. No matter how much faith you've got, it's still frightening. I know it shouldn't be, I feel I have let God down because He tried so much to help, but the fear was still there. That's where counselling helped. The counsellor helped me realise who I am and why I was so afraid. Understanding these things helped me to use my faith and my own strength to overcome the fear.

Counselling

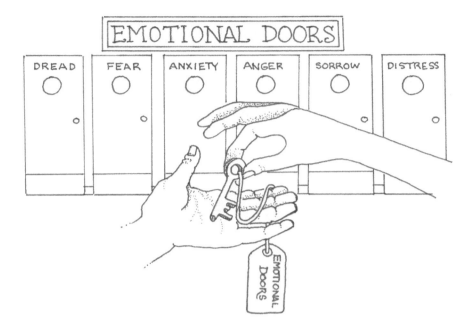

AS SOON AS I MET THE COUNSELLOR, I knew I could tell her everything. Also, I knew she would not judge me. I could tell her about my fears, my faith, and lots of things I could not tell other people. The fear was not knowing. When you get the thought that the cancer could still kill you, it's out of your hands. No matter how much faith you've got, it's still frightening. I know it shouldn't be, I feel I have let God down because He tried so much to help, but the fear was still there. That's where counselling helped.

THE COUNSELLOR enabled me to think about things that I had not recognised as important to my feelings, and to understand their significance. It was very helpful, also, to learn that it was not unusual to feel unsettled and insecure after finishing treatment.

110

A YEAR AFTER MY TREATMENT FINISHED, my husband was still stuck. He's a private sort of person who likes to deal with things on his own and he couldn't, and he didn't know which direction to go. My daughter and I were moving on, but he wasn't. Then one day, I got a surprise phone call from him at work. He said, "Would you think bad of me if I said I'm going for some counselling?" Of course my answer was, 'Absolutely not' – and since he had counselling, he's a changed person and we both wish he'd done it a year before.

I WAS DUE TO HAVE CHEMOTHERAPY, but I was down in the dumps and felt very negative. There had been a lot of cancer in my family and they had all had chemotherapy, but none had benefited from it; for whatever reason, it had done no good at all. I therefore decided it was not going to work for me, so I would not have any more treatment and would just take the time I had left and enjoy myself. I didn't realise how depressed I was and that what I was saying was ridiculous.

When I had almost decided I was not going to have the chemotherapy, my close friend, who stuck with me through it all, suggested I should get some help from somewhere else, perhaps from a cancer support centre. I thought it would be pointless: nobody had helped me so far, so why would anybody else? What could a 'support centre' do? When we first went in, there were several other people there and I felt very uncomfortable because I would have to admit I had cancer which I didn't want to do. However, from the atmosphere in the place, I quickly realised that I would not be persuaded to do anything I didn't want; I would not have to listen to someone telling me what I should do. Someone offered us a cup of tea and showed us round. Then, when we got back to the sitting room they said, "Do you think you would like to use any of our services?"

How wonderful was that? I was not a charity case, I was not being given something because I was a poor woman with cancer, I was not someone who had to be grateful for everything that came my way, I did not have to do as I was told. For the first time, I was offered a choice. Here was a place I could say what I feared, ask what I did not know, and that would be all right.

As I started speaking about it, I realised that what I needed was to make a decision – was I going to have the treatment? – but that was a decision I could not make on my own. I needed to talk to someone about it and the offer of talking with a counsellor seemed a good idea. The other thing was that had I gone to my GP for counselling, I would have had to wait for several months, but here I met a counsellor the next day, on a Saturday. How amazing was that? For me, it was just incredible. Not only was there an offer of help, but the help actually came. With cancer, lots of people offer, but nothing ever happens, or there is a waiting list, or they forget.

Talking with the counsellor helped me realise where my fear had come from, why I had this resistance to treatment and that it was not unreasonable to have that reluctance. I had always been in control of my life, but with cancer that changed. You're not in control of cancer, or its treatment, and you feel you're not in control of anything. That's what made it scary. Making a decision for myself gave me back some control. I decided to have the chemotherapy and I hope it's done me some good. Looking back, if I hadn't gone to the support centre, I would not have had any chemotherapy and my life would have been very different.

IN TEN YEARS, I had lost too many people close to me, mostly with cancer. I had never grieved and that had taken its toll. Finally, when a close friend died of cancer, so much had happened before without being resolved, there was no more emotional room for me to carry on without grieving and that took me over the edge.

By the time I walked in to meet the counsellor, I had lost all self-confidence and all self-esteem. I looked at the floor and could not make eye contact. As someone who had no idea what counselling would be like, I did not know what to expect. At my first meeting with the counsellor, I cried for nearly an hour.

To start with, I thought nothing much was happening, but the counsellor was very skilled, slowly helping me to open the emotional doors I had closed. She didn't give me answers to my problem, but she knew how to help me to find my own solutions. Sometimes it was uncomfortable and very difficult, but once I understood what she was doing, I accepted that she would be able to help. By the time I finished counselling, I was able to accept what had happened to me, I accepted the way I had reacted and the way I was, and I accepted that there was no stigma attached to it. I had also been given the skills to deal with my situation. My last session was completely different from the first; I could feel the difference and people said they could see a change in me. Someone who did not know I had counselling commented, "Oh, we've got Jay back."

AFTER MY HUSBAND DIED, when I was at my lowest ebb, I went to the local cancer support centre. The support, friendship and counselling I found has carried me through an extremely difficult time. I had professional counselling skills myself and so was aware of the possible benefits, but the support and focus given to me by the work facilitated by the counsellor has been absolutely priceless. To date, I am coping and hope to continue independently in the near future, but without the lifeline provided by the counsellor, I believe I would not be in the place I am today.

Money

FINANCE WAS A MASSIVE PROBLEM, a really massive problem. I've worked all my life since leaving school, apart from just six weeks, and here we were, asking, "How are we going to live?" Within days, my income fell from over £400 a week to sick pay of £87 and then that stopped after seven months. We managed to get through that period by prioritising what was really essential – the car and the motorbike had to go and they went, one thing less to worry about. After that, we went through the long process of applying for benefits, the PIP and all that (Personal Independence Payment). The PIP took ten months to be assessed and sorted. When it did eventually come through, they owed me £4,000 and working tax credit owed me £2,000. If it hadn't been for my brother who stumped up some money, we would have been right in it! We wouldn't have been able to pay the bills and put food on the table. Now, I've paid my brother back, caught up with all the bills and settled down. Now that we know where we are, we can manage and pay our way.

WORK AND MONEY, or lack of it, has been a problem ever since I was diagnosed. We had some savings and my wife has kept working, but we had to tighten our belt and our savings were being used up; they weren't going to last long.

At the time I was diagnosed, oil prices were falling and the North Sea oil business was already going down. Three weeks after I was diagnosed with cancer, the company paid me off. They said they no longer had a job for me. I was entitled to sick pay, but what they actually said was that I would be better off claiming sick benefit from the government rather than claiming from them. On reflection, I should have tried to fight them, but when you've got no money coming in and you're trying to cope with the cancer, what can you do?

When I discovered an experienced welfare benefits advisor, her help lifted a huge weight off our shoulders. There's this thing call PIP (Personal Independence Payment) that we didn't understand, but she explained it and helped with the form. Eventually it came through after six months, but that's a weird system. If we hadn't had some savings, I don't know what we would have done. We've helped some other people since then in the same situation because we know what they're struggling with. The stress of not having any money coming in for months when you're trying to cope with the cancer, not knowing what's going on with your PIP application, and hoping your money is not going to run out, is terrible.

The company has promised to take me back on the rigs, but they haven't made an offer yet, so I'll believe it when I get the phone call.

WHEN I STARTED THE CHEMO AND COULDN'T WORK, I was paid my salary for four weeks. After that, I was on sick benefit until I started work again, just £82 a week. I gave myself six weeks' rest after the chemotherapy and then went back to work. I wasn't fit to work, but I had to. I still had bad days, so each week or so, I would take a day or two of holiday till I felt strong enough to do the job properly again. By the time I had the fifth cycle of chemo, I had used up all my savings – sick benefit didn't pay the rent of £600 a month, so we were about to become homeless. I felt dreadful and went to the office at the Town Hall. How degrading. The housing application needed a medical report from my GP. She provided it, but it cost £30. What a disgrace! Fortunately, my nurse helped me fill in a form for a grant from Macmillan Cancer Support to help pay the electricity and gas bills; that was an amazing help. The Council staff worked quickly and I was offered a council house two weeks after the chemo finished. Not what we would have wanted, but there was no choice. There is nothing you can do, it all just happens.

MY HUSBAND had been in the oil industry, so we were very comfortable and I never had to provide for myself. Nine years before I was diagnosed with cancer we divorced and then two years before all this, although I was enjoying my well-paid job in industry, I thought that perhaps I should do something different, something to help other people: I became a carer for people in their homes. It was hard, I had not done anything like it before and I had to work all hours to keep up the money, but I loved it. When I needed to go for hospital appointments, I took an hour off. Even when they told me I had cancer, I went back to work the next day because I needed the money.

WHEN THEY TOLD ME I had cancer I tried to take it all in my stride, but I worried that it might not work out well in the future: I needed to prepare things for my wife, just in case, but I didn't want her to know that I was worried. I sorted out the practical things like the bank, the pensions and using the critical sickness insurance to pay off the mortgage. When the cheque came to close the mortgage, she burst into tears because she was convinced that the insurance company knew more than we did and that the future was not going to be good; she would rather be confident that I would still be fit and able to work and pay it off ourselves in due time. I was celebrating, but my wife thought it was a death sentence.

I tried to do things in a roundabout way so that my wife wouldn't be concerned, but she saw through that and knew exactly what was happening. We have a biggish garden, with a lot of grass, and I knew she wouldn't manage a lawn mower if I wasn't there: it would have to be paved. We went to the builders merchant to choose the stone together, which we did, but I realise now that it made my wife feel sad because she knew why we were doing it, and she was thinking they would be my tombstones.

MY WIFE will struggle and will have to work again when I'm not here, so I'm planning things to be as good as possible for her. I've been paying off loans and doing things in the house so she will not have to worry about her home when I'm gone. The various contracts and banking that were in my name we have transferred to my wife and on the computer we have changed my passwords to passwords she will be able to remember instead. One of the first things we did was plan my funeral. We haven't needed it yet, but it's organised for when the time comes. Now that everything has been done that will need to be done it's a good feeling in one way, but it's not really, because I wish I had the feeling that I wasn't going to die. But these are the cards I've been dealt and I'll try and bluff them for as long as I can.

How long do you think I have?

WHEN MY MALIGNANT MELANOMA RECURRED, I knew the doctors might slow it down, but they would not be able to cure it. I saw three different members of the oncology team in four weeks and I asked each of them what my prognosis was: "How long do you think I have?" They were very reluctant to answer and it seemed I had to drag the information out of them. One said six to nine months, one twelve to fifteen months, and the third eighteen months to two years 'but do not be surprised if it's only three months'. I understand their reluctance because melanoma is very unpredictable, but I needed to know. Although they gave different answers, it was clear I didn't have very long.

Two years before, my wife had noticed a mole on my back that had changed and turned out to be a malignant melanoma. It was treated by the removal of a wide circle of skin about five inches in diameter, which showed no remaining cancer cells. I went for the regular checkups and wasn't worried in the slightest. Earlier in my life, I had served in the army for twelve years in the Royal Engineers and the Logistics Corps in Cyprus, Falklands, Bosnia, Germany and the Gulf. My sister died and then my mother had a severe stroke leaving her in a wheelchair with nobody to care for her so, in 2002, I decided to leave the army and found work as a taxi driver. This provided the flexibility to be my mother's carer as well as work.

In July 2014, I started feeling pains in my ribs which I put down to lifting wheelchairs in and out of the taxi, but it didn't get any better and eventually an x-ray showed a shadow on the lung. A needle biopsy suggested it was malignant melanoma and scans then showed it was not in the lung, but in my ribs, spine, shoulder and thigh. The melanoma had come back. That was on 23rd December. A friend had died of melanoma a few years before and there had been no effective treatment for him, so we didn't have the greatest Christmas. The pains were much worse and some days I could hardly get off the settee. However, a new immunotherapy was made available to me and the pain relief it gave was like a new lease of life! I was like a new person and we were able to get away for a holiday that I thought previously would not be possible. After four cycles, a chest x-ray showed the previous shadow and the cancer in the ribs had disappeared! Unfortunately, scans gave the bad news that two new lesions had grown elsewhere in my lungs and I would need different treatment.

Once again, a new research immunotherapy was offered, but when the preliminary tests were done my tumours did not fit the research criteria. I was really down after that, because what they were saying was that I had to get worse before they could try making me better! Fortunately, a third drug had just been approved which would be guaranteed for two years provided it continued to work and I've been on that for five cycles. We have been able to get away again and I have managed a few rounds of golf; sometimes I have to remind myself that I am supposed to be terminally ill! It doesn't matter, but I have been putting in a new kitchen which involved carrying heavy boxes of tiles, although I know I need to be sensible with the cancer in the spine. At other times, just recently, I have become very tired and I think the cancer is growing again, but then I think it might be due to the medication – we don't know. I'm due for another scan which will show whether or not the cancer has progressed. We are off to Cyprus for a week, but we only plan a month ahead as we never know how I will be and I cannot get travel insurance.

People are surprised that I can be so upbeat about it, but worrying or giving up is not going to make it any better. I have my wife and three grandchildren with whom I want to spend as much time as I possibly can. By the time I was told I had terminal cancer, the pain had interfered with driving and I decided to stop work altogether. I had seen my friend die and I decided that if I only had six months left, I wanted to spend it with my family. I still hope the drugs will work and the cancer will go away, but nobody knows, so there is only one solution: live life to the full while I can. Being realistic, the time will come when I cannot take the grandchildren to the park and play with them on the beach, so I do it while I can. We want to visit the Grand Canyon, but I'm not fit enough just now; if I'm still here next year, we will go then. In the meantime, there are plenty of other places and other things to be getting on with.

There is a lot of uncertainty and to plan what's left is difficult. When you go to hospital, the doctors give you the results and tell you what they want you to know, but that's not necessarily what you need, so I carry a small diary in which I write the questions I need to ask as well as reminders of appointments. It's also a great help for our social life: what with treatment, blood tests, scans, family and seeing all the old friends who have come out of the woodwork since they heard what's happened, life is very busy.

I have already had my wake! When I was diagnosed and we thought I had so little time left, I wanted to have one last drink with my friends from the army days and work. Before the first treatment, friends came from all over, even from Gibraltar. There were a hundred of us, and we had an amazing night out together. Now they feel cheated, not because I'm still here, but because with all the fundraising I do for Cancer Connections they keep hearing, 'This may be the last thing I can do, so dig deep,' and they've heard all that before! Before I had cancer, I contributed to charities, but never cancer charities because they got so much compared with some other diseases. Now, having cancer myself and experiencing all the help my wife and I have received, I do as much as I can to give something back.

Counselling is something I have not needed, but I could see that my wife was struggling; she still finds it hard every day. She needed somewhere to cry, to swear, to be angry and she would never do that at home, because she wanted to be strong for me. Seeing a counsellor let her do that and it was a great help. We don't talk about the cancer now, we've done all the talking, but we have discussed sorting out practical family things.

To anyone else who is given a terminal diagnosis, I would say, 'Your life isn't over yet, make your preparations, don't put things off, then make the most of each day as it comes'. To the oncologists I would say, 'Try to be more open and be prepared to talk with us honestly. Then organise treatments for the patients so they are arranged and coordinated properly so we spend as little time at hospital as possible; we have lives to get on with'.

Oh, by the way, from my army days I have a big tattoo on my back of the Grim Reaper which was caught up in the surgery to remove the melanoma. Now that it's healed, he's been decapitated! We'll see.

One happy fella

*It was over six years ago that Tony noticed his voice was getting weak.
Visits to his doctor, various hospital clinics, x-rays, scans and endoscopy eventually
made the diagnosis, but by that time, he had lost weight and was experiencing difficulty
with swallowing.*

IKNEW I HAD CANCER OF THE LARYNX and I knew that surgery was the only hope of cure, but I had decided against it. When the letter came for me to go into hospital I decided, once again, that I would not go. However, three days before the admission date, my wife was taken into hospital as an emergency. On the Sunday night as I left her at the end of visiting, she said, "Make sure you have that operation" – and, for her, I did. The next day, I went to the hospital, had all the tests and the following day had the operation: nine hours. They told me it was a very severe form of cancer, but they had removed it all, including my voice box and the lymph nodes. When I came round, I tried to speak, forgetting what they had said, and nothing came out. After two days in intensive care, I returned to the ward and it was only then that it dawned on me what had actually happened.

With all the drugs I was on, I couldn't write clearly to ask questions, but all this time my wife was in another hospital and I needed to know how she was. When I finally made the sister understand, there was no answer, but before long, I had visitors, the whole family, including the grandchildren. I knew immediately something was up, something was wrong. My wife had died.

I went to pieces and tried to pull all the tubes out. The nurses put me back to bed and made sure two of them stayed with me through the night; they were scared I might do something. I was upset because I felt guilty: I should have been with her, I should have been there to say goodbye to my wife, and I wasn't. The nurses and the hospital team were wonderful and did their best to help me, but I was devastated and started to go downhill.

By the time I came home, I felt everyone was staring at me, at my neck, and I couldn't get that out of my mind. Not being able to speak, I had to write everything down and that was incredibly frustrating; it's impossible to describe how that feels. People were talking to me, but I couldn't say anything to them. It made me angry and I felt a freak.

Not long after, I was told I needed radiotherapy. Although I was clear of cancer from the operation, there was still a chance that it might come back. I said no, I'd had enough. My daughter said yes. I gave in and had thirty-two treatments. It nearly killed me, but I saw people worse than me and I felt a fraud.

As time went on, my neck began to heal, but I became increasingly depressed, really depressed. I couldn't communicate, it was six months before anybody could understand me on the phone, and it was difficult to eat. I was nineteen stone when I went into hospital and in a few months I was down to thirteen. I had started driving again, but I was driving at stupid speeds and I didn't care; that's how the depression got to me. The doctor arranged for me to have counselling and that was a great help. The counsellor was patient and slowly helped me to understand why I was behaving as I was, which was what I needed.

At the hospital, I was also seeing a wonderful speech and language therapist who helped me and got me using a voice simulator – a gadget you press on your neck that speaks for you, but makes you sound like a Dalek. The wounds healed, too, but I still had a tracheostomy, a hole in my neck, and had to wear a dressing, a sort of collar, instead of a tie. If I couldn't wear a tie, I wasn't properly dressed and that upset me because I always like to be smartly dressed.

It's four years now since the operation and I'm seventy-nine. I've come to terms with what happened and everything else in my life. I've still got a tracheostomy with a valve and a button at the front that I have to push when I want to speak. People still get impatient when they can't hear me easily me on the phone. Sometimes the valve plays up and it's embarrassing and frustrating. I would prefer you to look at me and not my neck, but if you want to look at it, look at it, I don't give a damn. That's how it is now, but at the time, I thought I would never live through it. That first year was the worst I have ever lived.

One night, after an evening out with friends and feeling really happy, I arrived home and headed for the front door. Suddenly it seemed as if I hit a brick wall and couldn't put one foot in front of the other. I could not go in the house: the lights were off and my wife was not there. Instead, I slept in the car for three nights at the top of the cliffs overlooking the sea. Each night I thought about what would happen if I wasn't here, I thought about the grandchildren and my daughter, but it came to the stage when I thought this should not be happening to me. I'd had a great life, fifty-three years of a good marriage, but I buried my wife on our wedding anniversary. Why was this happening? I had seen my friends who had cancer go before me, so why should I be here when they'd all gone?

By the third night, I'd decided that was it and I was ready to go over the top. I put the car in gear, let the hand brake off, revved up and – it was then that I had what I can only describe as an out of body experience. I saw myself outside the car looking in and asking, "What are you doing? What are you doing?" and it frightened the hell out of me. It hit me right in the face: "Don't be stupid, Tony, get yourself together!" I switched the engine off, put the hand brake on, got out of the car and walked round it, and could see that I was no longer inside. That was the turning point. After a while, I got back in, drove home, and went to bed. It was 3am.

It was the nurse specialist at the hospital who told me about Cancer Connections. I decided to give it a try and when I went in the atmosphere in the place was wonderful; it was the most comfortable place I had found in months. I met the manager first and talking with her she started me back on the right track. I could call in whenever I liked and knew I would be welcome. The volunteers knew if I was down and they would let me talk about it. Up to then, I'd kept everything to myself, I had never spoken about my wife since she died, and I could do that, too. They listened and were patient. I've carried our wedding photograph with me for fifty-seven years and I felt able to show it to them, and they loved it. That place saved my life.

A few months ago, at the routine follow-up appointment with the surgeon, I decided to ask him what the chances were that the cancer might come back; I'd never had the courage to ask him before. His reply was all I needed to hear: "Tony, you're clear, ninety-nine percent cured." Well, that's good enough for me and I have to say it's given me a new confidence. I'm one happy fella.

Joyce did not want to know

OUR NEXT DOOR NEIGHBOUR'S father had lung cancer and he'd survived five years; Joyce decided she was going to have five years, too. She had a good group of friends and after she had recovered from the initial distress, she plucked up enough courage to tell them. She didn't talk about it much, but by the next week they had each knitted a little square and made a special blanket for her. She wrapped it round and used it almost every day and at her funeral it lay on her casket.

We had talked about this sort of situation before and Joyce had always said, "If ever I'm terminally ill, I will not want to know." After we received the letter from the hospital, I did look on the internet because I wanted to understand all the medical shorthand, but when the website said, 'If you don't want to know any more, log off now', I logged off. I did not want to know anything that I could not share with my wife. Knowing things and trying to hide them would make our relationship difficult for me, which was not what we needed. It became obvious that she would not have five years, but I was able to cope with that and we did not have to talk about it. For the first few months life went on, we were not morbid or miserable, we laughed and joked a lot and we were both very positive. We had a boat on the river and used to sail every weekend, but as her illness progressed, it wasn't really possible. We managed a few short trips, but one has a routine on board and Joyce did not have the strength to do the tasks that you need a second person to do. She had chemotherapy and radiotherapy, but to no avail, although the oncologist was very understanding and always boosted Joyce at the follow-up appointments which made her feel so much better.

In some ways, when it spread to her brain and she became forgetful, I was quite pleased that her awareness became less; it made it easier for me. At first I thought she had Alzheimer's as well as the cancer, but the true cause was soon apparent and confirmed by the doctors. She never knew and was never distressed; she was content trying to do the crossword although she did not get the clues, and laughing while she tried, not very successfully, to help with the cooking. It didn't stop us going out.

Her breathlessness stopped her walking up hill, but we worked round that, too. If we took the Metro to Haymarket it was all downhill to the river and we could stop off for coffee or a meal, or a champagne tea, at lots of places on the way down. At the bottom there was a bus that would take us to another station where there was an escalator and our car was parked outside! It was a small military operation, but it worked and we were able to do it until six weeks before she died.

Joyce was very brave. It was only in the last ten days when she couldn't get up the stairs that we slept downstairs. We obtained a hospital-type bed which was good and we managed very well on our own, just the two of us, until the nurses started coming regularly, thirty-six hours before she died. I kept a spreadsheet of exactly what was going on, what food and drink she had, what doses of Oramorph I was administering. I went round to the doctor every two or three days to show him, to check everything, and he would adjust doses accordingly. Between us, we were able to care for Joyce very well.

I had been given offers of help, but didn't need them till the last few hours. She died on the Monday, but the previous Tuesday she had eaten the small breakfast, lunch and dinner I had prepared. The nurses knew I was up most of the night and would need some sleep, so they offered a night nurse, but I declined. I knew I would be upstairs wide awake in any case, so there was no point.

Then Joyce reached the point when she had stopped taking any food and was taking very little liquid; she could no longer speak and seemed to be slipping away. She had a syringe driver for medication and the nurses came and went as needed; they were lovely and were most helpful. On the Sunday evening, they were with her and I asked if they would mind if I had a small glass of white wine. The nurse then asked Joyce if she would like a sip of wine and a lovely smile spread over her face. So the nurse took the syringe and gave her some, and there was another smile. That was the last sign of awareness before she passed away eight hours later. Her breathing stopped and started, stopped and started, just as the nurses said it would. Then it stopped. I held her in my arms and then called the nurses. Joyce had always said she would not want to go to hospital to die. Even on our second date, she said, "Don't die before me, will you?" I'm pleased to say, both of her wishes were fulfilled.

I'll go ahead and put the kettle on

Philip, a retired surgeon, and Betty, a retired senior nurse, had been good friends for over thirty years. As Philip recounts when Betty's cancer returned, her approach was, as always, practical and well organised.

IN THE SUMMER of 2012, Betty mentioned that she had a lump beneath her lower jaw. It didn't seem to be anything very much, but when it persisted some tests were needed and a biopsy was undertaken. We then enjoyed a brief holiday while awaiting events. Alas, the news was not encouraging: Betty had fairly extensive involvement of her lymphatic system with non-Hodgkin lymphoma which would require several months of chemotherapy. A suitable wig was found and the chemotherapy was completed. After five months, she was pronounced tumour free, which she took to indicate a cure.

We then had a very successful year with no problems at all, until some backache developed while we were away on holiday. We were able to walk six miles each day and we had a very pleasant time, but when we returned home further scans showed a recurrence of the disease. We were told that much more intensive chemotherapy would be required. This lasted from July to the end of November and was exceedingly disabling; Betty was very ill and, on occasions, she did think about stopping the treatment, but decided to see it through and by Christmas, felt well.

Soon after we were able to visit her daughter in New Zealand, but we both recognised that time might be limited and made plans accordingly. We were able to visit Swaledale again and to join our friends in April for a tour of Chester Zoo. By this time, Betty had developed a limp and accepted the offer of a wheelchair.

The limp persisted and led to more scans and a consultation with a neurologist. It was thought there might be some treatable abnormality pressing on the nerves in the spinal column and a neurosurgical exploration was offered. Before this could be carried out, Betty developed double vision which led to an urgent consultation with the very courteous and sympathetic medical oncologist who explained that the problem was due to recurrent disease in the central nervous system, that could not be cured by surgery or reached by chemotherapy, and that no further treatment was practical. We were advised to make the best of the last few weeks or months, returning to the clinic if we needed further advice.

Leaving the clinic, we set off in the car towards Betty's village, driving in silence as we often did. Part of the way home, she said, "Well, it looks as though I'm going to go first. I'll go ahead and put the kettle on, but don't be long." When we got home, she said, "I think it's time to plan my funeral, and I would like my daughter over from New Zealand whilst I am still reasonably well." It was now early June.

Within a few days we had both daughters and the retired Methodist minister in the lounge of her cottage. Betty had a clear idea of what she wanted and the arrangements were soon agreed. She also had a large number of photographs from which she selected the ones she would like to be shown in the church before the service, together with appropriate music. At this stage, we all knew that there would be a continuing process of gradual decline. We didn't need to discuss it, it was occurring, we just went from one day to the next.

On one occasion, we did discuss if she would have had this more intensive treatment, which made her so ill, if she had known how distressing it would be, but she didn't really come to a conclusion about that. She did have a little extra normal life, her backache did improve, she enjoyed Christmas and she did have her daughter with her for a while, but it was not the extra year that she hoped for. She was ill for four months, for what became three months of normal health before her decline. It was also during this time that her mental attitude changed: she no longer thought, 'I'm cured'. Although she was told, once again, after the chemotherapy, that there was no evidence of disease, she did start to wonder when it might come back.

During the majority of this time, the last two months, despite increasing disability, Betty looked after herself, always fully dressed with her usual make up, receiving her many visitors in her own home. She remained concerned for those around her, but gradually became housebound which frustrated her. At this stage, a member of the family or a friend stayed overnight. Routine became very important for her, including cocoa at night with someone reading at least one chapter of a book of her choice.

A week before her death, her lack of mobility was such that we needed some professional help. One phone call to her GP was sufficient. The Critical Care Team arrived and took over the changing and lifting needed over the last few days. It was thought an NHS bed would help, but this would not go up the narrow stone stairs in this old cottage. It could go in the lounge, but how would we get Betty down the stairs? One of the team said, "Betty can't do it, we can't do it and the ambulance men won't. However, we can always get the Fire Brigade; they will do it as a training exercise."

In reality, the Fire Brigade were not needed as Betty was not well enough to move. She had become chesty and slept most of the time. She died the next day, as she had wished, in her own bed, in her own bedroom and with the view from it of the village which she loved, with her daughters and me at her side.

* * *

The little chapel on the hill was packed: latecomers stood both inside and outside. While we waited, we listened to her favourite music and smiled at the numerous photographs from Betty's childhood and teenage years, her family, holidays, colleagues and friends. After the service, we gathered in the sunshine outside the village hall and enjoyed a generous tea, just as Betty had arranged.

We didn't want any fuss

DURING MY WORKING LIFE as an electrical engineer, I had visited forty different countries and we had lived in twelve different homes. However, during all this time, my wife and I were never separated for more than three or four weeks at a time.

When I was fifty-six, I gave up full time work, which was the best thing I ever did because we then had thirteen wonderful years together. When I was younger, my wife had to hold everything in the family together, which she did fantastically; when I retired, I said, "Now it's your turn, I'm going to look after you." When she developed lung cancer, it was my desire to look after her then, too. Now, since she's gone, that's what I miss: I have nobody to look after, no one to mollycoddle.

It was the Macmillan nurse at the hospital who told us about Cancer Connections when we first heard the diagnosis, but we didn't understand what it was all about. We used to pass the building on the way to the hospital every time we went for an appointment, but we didn't know what to expect. I think, also, that my wife was reluctant to seek any outside help because she had this feeling (wrongly, in my opinion) that the cancer was her fault. However, one day, I stopped the car and said we would pop in for a minute. As we walked in, the manager greeted us and immediately we felt at home. We went into a quiet room, my wife had a little cry and it was as though a switch had been flicked: this was a place worth coming to. We didn't want a fuss, we wanted support – and that is what we found.

When Joyce was dying, the district nurses came and looked after her wonderfully and, when she passed away, they were there in ten minutes. We had funeral expenses insurance, so I asked them to telephone the undertaker and she was taken away within the hour. The following morning, on my way to buy the paper as usual, I went across the road to tell our neighbours. A few minutes later they called, but found that my wife was not there. "Are you not keeping her here?" they asked in rather shocked surprise. The answer was a simple 'No' – for me that was not an option. I held her when she died and until the undertaker arrived, but I had to let her go. Then my grieving could start.

I have an allotment and the day after she died, I moved thirty wheelbarrows full of manure from the communal pile to my plot, because I have always found strenuous exercise clears the brain. That helped me to deal with my initial grief. However, the strange thing is that the grieving didn't start in earnest until the Faith Hope and Love Walk for the local charity five months later. When the Mayor started us all off on the walk, it really hit me: my wife should have been with me and she wasn't. I cried all the way round the park. I had often cried before the walk, but I don't think I had been accepting my wife was gone.

I still go in for a coffee and a chat. I've never felt the need for counselling, but the ambience and talking with people is a comfort. Several weeks ago, when I was having reflexology, we were talking about anything and nothing, but we got on about crying and the therapist said, "If you burst into tears, I can't give you a hug because you'll stop crying and you have to cry it out." Before, when I started to cry, I said to myself 'Pull yourself together' and stopped, but a week ago, I didn't stop and I sobbed for two hours, and I've been a lot better since. It will come back again, I've no doubt, there will be some rough times and some not so rough times, but I have to get on with it and make the best of a bad job.

It took me a long time to pick up the ashes from the undertaker and I did so on the spur of the moment. I thought I would scatter them in the park round the corner where she used to play as a child, but I've decided not to do that. They are going to stay in my home and when I die, it's in my will that both our ashes will be scattered in the same park and we'll be together.

For the future? I look forward to a new chapter in life. It will be different. There are some things I cannot do yet because they are too raw; I cannot face them yet because she won't be there. I never used to have a daily routine, but now I go for a brisk two mile walk and then read the paper. If the weather's half decent, I go to the allotment and then I see how the day pans out. One thing is for sure, I will not mope and with the help of friends, I will have some great days in the future.

Left in the world
without the love of my life

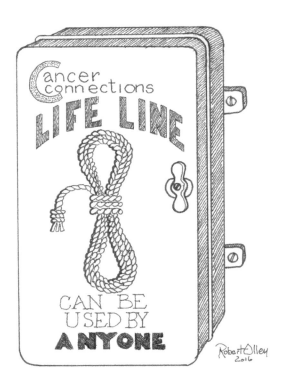

THE SIX YEARS since my husband was first diagnosed with cancer, leading ultimately to his death just over two years ago, have been the worst years of my life. His initial diagnosis resulted in an almost paralysing fear which had to be hidden from him at all costs. No negativity was allowed to encroach into our lives and I can recall being congratulated from all sides for the strength I showed and the support I offered him in his darkest hours. This included attending all appointments, staying with him for as long as I was allowed whilst he was a patient in hospital, feeding and caring for him at home, giving up my career to ensure his quality of life was as good as it could be at home and ultimately being with him when he passed away.

Following the initial shock, I was left in a world without my best friend, the person who had been the love of my life for twenty-five years. What was I to do with no one and nothing to focus on? I had left my career which was my vocation and as a woman of fifty, deeply traumatised by the death of her husband, I questioned seriously what life had to offer me. I no longer felt able to pick up the threads of my life again. There were so many issues to be faced, not least the loneliness I felt as a widow without children. Support is often available initially, but with the best will in the world, most people seem to have the idea that '*it's over a year, she should have got over it by now*'! I now know that there is no 'getting over' the pain I feel at the loss of a wonderful man who can never be replaced! However, with a counsellor's help, I have returned to work, socialise with friends and am once again able to play a supportive role for other members of my family.

I had regular counselling sessions from the death of my husband for several months by which time I felt able to cope more effectively with life as it is now. However, following a difficult period a few months later, I felt the need to contact the counsellor again. That decision was not taken lightly, but I am so grateful that I was able, once again, to avail myself of a service which I can best describe as second to none. Thank you.

Saying goodbye

I'm due to go soon

When I was admitted to hospital they told me it was pneumonia, but when I went back a few weeks later they said I had lung cancer. I haven't had any treatment and that was four months ago. I'm a bit short of breath, but otherwise I'm fine and look after myself. I make a very good chicken broth and my daughter gives me meals for the freezer.

How do I feel about it? Well, the doctor said I'm very fit and I feel it. I'm eighty-seven, so I'm due to go soon. I'm not worried.

Letter to a friend

Thank you for the scenic book on Skye. It was uplifting for me during my stay in hospital. It brought back some memorable events of the time we spent there. One memory triggers another, all equally enjoyable. Unfortunately, things will come to an end soon as treatment for my complaint has been terminated due to lack of response. So, I await the inevitable. However, I am at present fit and well – and looking at life for more challenges.

And a final note for the Vicar

I would like to thank the people I have had the privilege and pleasure of meeting through my lifetime, particularly those who have given me support through their thoughts and deeds during the latter and final stages. Anne and I have enjoyed our lives together and both feel it has ended much too early. However, both of us would probably feel the same way in twenty years' time. It must be difficult to talk about someone you have never met or heard of, though that may be rectified in the near future. Many thanks in anticipation.

Remembering Nanna

Mary passed away on 2nd February 2012. She had four grandchildren:
Josh, Olivia, Emily and Eliza.

OLIVIA WAS NINE years old at the time. She and her mum lived with Mary. Cousin Emily, who was ten, and her sister Eliza, who was six, lived in Sheffield and the journey to see their grandma took about three hours each way. That meant they could not go to see her very often, but they loved to talk on the phone and they always had a wonderful time together when she came to stay.

'She came loads of times. We do shows at our dancing school and she used to come to all of them. Once, she was at the hospital and they wanted to keep her in, but she told them that she wasn't going to stay because she had to come to Sheffield on the train to see our show. That was more important to her than staying in hospital.

'Even when she got quite poorly she would take the train to see us, but then it got a bit too much so we Skyped her instead. It was strange at first, but we liked to see her on the computer and tell her things. We got help from some friends to buy a laptop for her so she could Skype and do shopping on-line, and she really loved it because she could watch Coronation Street in bed!'

As the cancer advanced, it became clear that Mary was dying. Her daughter in Sheffield understood the seriousness of the situation and visited frequently, but was seldom able to bring the girls with her. Like many other parents facing death in the family, she was unsure how much her girls should know and was reluctant to upset them, so she told them very little. Mary was always bright and cheerful on the phone and gave her grandchildren no clue how ill she was.

Emily remembers, *'I think I had quite a good idea, because Mum went to see Nanna every time she could and I just thought, "Why is she going all the time if she isn't that bad?" And we used to miss Mum a lot. We did talk about it between us, but when we first heard that Nanna was very ill, we were really shocked. We knew she had had cancer before, when we were younger, but that had gone away, so when it came back again it was a shock. She had all the right treatment for it and it wasn't supposed to come back. Nobody in our family had cancer, and nobody at school had cancer, so we didn't know about it.*

'By about November time, Nanna was not very well and we began to get worried and were scared that she might not get better, but at the same time, we kept hoping she would.'

For Olivia, it was different. Living with her grandmother, it was obvious that she was not well. With neighbours and friends calling to see her, and the nurses coming and going every day as well, even as a young girl, she realised it must be something serious.

'She had an oxygen mask and there was a stair lift. I asked Auntie Steph questions like "Why are all the nurses here?" because I wanted to know. And then when I wanted to be with Nanna, there were all these other people coming and I felt a bit fed up because she was my Nanna. I didn't mind really because when her sister, my Auntie Ann, came round to see her, my uncle and me did jigsaws downstairs and we hid the pieces and he'd have to find them.'

However, her Nanna being poorly didn't stop them having lots of fun together, especially when Emily and Eliza visited. Because of the chemotherapy Mary had received, she was still wearing a wig.

'All of us tried it on, taking it in turns. We had fantastic fun with it. It was brown which was okay for Nanna, but it didn't suit me and everyone said it made me look like my mum! She kept it on a wig stand in the kitchen so we used to colour it in and stick big eyelashes on, to make it look all pretty.

'Nanna had her boobie off as well, a long time ago. Like wearing her wig, it never

bothered her, but she kept losing the false boobie and we all had to go looking for it. She was quite big, so it was quite heavy and she didn't wear it most of the time. She just put it down, in the kitchen, anywhere. Then, if anyone was coming or she was going out, we would all have to "hunt the boobie" around the house. Whoever found it got a pound!

'We used to have fun on the stair lift as well. I used to sit on Olivia's knee going up, but Nanna could see us from her bed and used to tell us off. It was not easy for Nanna, though, because she wanted to come downstairs and her legs were very swollen which made getting on and off difficult.'

The laptop proved invaluable. Mary didn't just use it for watching Coronation Street and Skyping her grandchildren. She used it to do some important shopping. She had always been very organised and was not going to change just because she was ill. Presents for birthdays and Christmas were a must – and she ordered them all on-line when she was too unwell to go out. Her last Christmas was not going to be any different. She organised friends who were in touch with the top girl group 'Little Mix' to get autographed CDs for her bairns. Emily had been to one of their concerts and Olivia had met the girls when they made a surprise visit to Cancer Connections. Mary knew these were things that they would enjoy long after she had gone.

Cancer Connections had been a place of comfort and help for Mary during her illness. When she became very unwell, and the girls came to see her, they came too.

'It wasn't scary at all and we had a lovely time. We had a hand massage and a foot massage, which was very tickly. Then we talked about Nanna and the things we loved about her.'

Emily and Eliza remembered: *'When she used to come to us, she always brought presents and baked cakes with us which was fun. She brought jelly moulds with our names on and we still make jellies with them. Raspberry and strawberry are our favourites. She brought pretty, sparkly things, and one day she brought me some high-heeled shoes. My mum wouldn't let me wear those, but Nanna brought some for me anyway. Not very high, but they were high for me.'*

For Eliza, bath times were a special memory: *'Nanna had big, deep baths and I used to go in when I was little and we played with those swimmers, the ones you wind up and put in the water, and I used to love it.*

'Then there were the grass-heads! They looked like a potato man, but had grass seeds on their heads and you watered them to make the grass grow. When Nanna lost her hair, we had a competition with her to see whose would grow fastest. The grass-heads won, but she didn't mind.

'Before we left Cancer Connections, we each wrote down the ten things we loved about our Nanna and when we got home we put the pieces of paper on the wall by her bed as a

surprise for when she came home from the hospital. It made her very happy and she said she wanted them in her coffin with her so she could take them with her. We wanted to keep them, too, so Mum had some copies made for us.

'*After she died, when we were sorting everything out, we all took something of Nanna's that we wanted to keep.*' Emily chose Mary's memory foam V-pillow '*Because it had her smell on it.*' Olivia took one of Mary's teddy bears. '*She had loads of teddies, so I had the "Tickled Pink" one that had a T-shirt with the breast cancer campaign on it.*' Eliza had another of the teddy bears. '*It's lovely and cuddly and I use mine every night when I go to bed.*

'*We've got lots of photos of her and I talk to her in my head, and every night I still say, "I love you Nanna". We remember her birthday each year and write messages on balloons and then send them off. At school, sometimes in class, I start crying just thinking about Nanna, but the teachers take us out and talk to us and make sure I'm okay, and they comfort us and remind me she's in a better place now.*'

Eliza was too young to go to the funeral, but Emily and Olivia did. '*I begged Mum to let me go. I wanted to say my last goodbyes.*' '*And I read a prayer.*' '*We were pleased we went.*' '*Coming to Cancer Connections we did things for Nanna without realising it and we were helping her when she wasn't well. It also helped us understand she wouldn't get better, but in a nice way.*'

Faith, Hope and Love

Steven completed a Masters degree a year before moving to a new job elsewhere in the country as Operations Director of an international company. He was moving to his dream job but, if successful, it would involve moving his family and home a long way from Tyneside, so with his wife, Ashley, he agreed that he should go ahead to try the new position first. Their new daughter, Libby, was just eight weeks old and her sister, Eleanor, was four. On the second day he was taken ill and deep vein thrombosis was diagnosed. Returning home, new symptoms developed and after two weeks, he knew the worst: it was inoperable oesophago-gastric cancer. When it was suggested he should leave hospital, he refused. Ashley takes up the story.

STEVEN FELT he would not be able to protect his family if he returned home. Although we had been told lots of things about the cancer, nobody had ever said the word 'terminal', but a nurse let slip 'that's what we call terminal patients'. Before that, we thought he would be able to fight the cancer, so that word 'terminal' was a body blow. When we were referred to the cancer centre, the specialist agreed it was terminal because they would not be able to get rid of the cancer, but the hope was that he would be able to live with it, which was a completely different way of looking at things. He came home and started on some trial chemotherapy which he had for six months. The first three months were amazing, the chemo shrank everything, but in the next few months it started growing again and he went downhill very quickly. There was no other treatment worth trying, there was nothing more the hospital could do, so he was to go home and wait until he died.

This time, the specialist was very blunt with us and told Steven he needed to get his things in order. To this he had replied, "That may work for some people, but that's not how we deal with things; we are positive thinking and we will beat this," to which she replied, "You can't." She knew what she was talking about, but he was never going to accept that attitude. When they shut that door, Steven didn't go to pieces, which I thought he would, but we didn't know where to turn. I started to panic and looked for other options, anything, anywhere, that might do something. He walked a lot and found meditation helpful. Reiki healing was wonderful because it gave him so much peace and rest – he said it was amazing and indescribable and he loved it. He had insomnia and spent most of the night on his laptop. At the time, a friend was receiving treatment for breast cancer and she had insomnia from her chemotherapy, so they used to talk together through the night. Stephen and Amanda used to work together and we knew her husband, Simon, through other friends. I didn't know them well, but they helped each other a lot by chatting on-line.

We had our last Christmas together and we all went out for family lunch, but he was needing massive amounts of morphine and wasn't really there. He couldn't sit still and couldn't lie down. Our eldest daughter, Libby, developed pneumonia and I spent New Year with her in hospital, which made Steven furious because I wouldn't let him visit in case he caught something from the hospital. By this time there was a large lump in his side that was painful, but he wouldn't go to a doctor. He had an appointment booked with his favourite GP and refused to go earlier because he knew he would be admitted to hospital and he wasn't going to leave us at home until he really had to go. When she examined him, he admitted he was in pain and she said she would call an ambulance. Once again he refused, saying that he needed to go home first to see his kids. I took him home where, unbeknown to me, he said goodbye to our kids and goodbye to his mum. She said, "I'll see you when you come home," to which he replied, "I won't be coming home." With me and with his friends it was different: he was going to get better. Even that evening in hospital, he told a visitor he would be better soon. It was the only way he could deal with it, by saying he was going to be okay.

However, when he was admitted to hospital that last time, he sat on the bed and told me that he wanted me to meet somebody else, he didn't want to think of me being forever on my own, but I said, "Don't be so stupid, I married you and I'm going to stay married to you and there isn't any other option." At the time it was an awful conversation to have, but he said he needed to tell me that he wanted me to move on, for the kids' sake and for me. Looking back, I realise it was a wonderful conversation because it must have been hard for him to say what he did.

Steven had been a person who didn't trust people easily, but when he developed cancer he did a huge about-turn. His whole personality changed: he became more trusting, more open, more caring. When he was first diagnosed and was taking blood thinning drugs he stopped shaving. His friends felt useless because there seemed to be nothing they could do to help him, but they came up with the idea that they would also stop shaving for three months. They called it a Beardathon and fundraised for Cancer Connections. At the graduation ceremony for his degree, he had a huge beard and so did all his friends. He said once that his friends helping him had restored his faith in people and he even enjoyed life more. He lived life for 'now' not the future and died a more friendly person.

After we knew there could be no more medical treatment we went to see a specialist cancer nutritionist and although he was losing weight, Steven was keeping to a vegan diet, wheat grass and all sorts, and was still doing meditation and yoga. He loved the yoga and meditation, but not the diet, and when he knew he was going to hospital for the last time, I asked him want he wanted. The answer was a Dickson's saveloy, a pasty and a sandwich, so that's what I got and he ate the lot! When he reached the hospital, they gave him a packed lunch and he had Mars bars and crisps, all the things he hadn't eaten for weeks.

He was all right until the evening, although he couldn't get comfortable and despite all they gave him, he couldn't get rid of the pain. I stayed with him till about eleven o'clock and then drove home and went straight to bed, but during the night the nurse telephoned to say he had taken a turn for the worse. "He told me not to ring you, but you need to come." My sister came with me. In those few hours since I had seen him he had aged and he looked like an old man. He was up and down, the pain was still there and he fought and fought for several more hours. There seemed to be nothing they gave him that stopped the pain and I begged them to put him to sleep, but suddenly he relaxed. He knew I was there, but I'm not sure how aware he was. He lay down and it seemed he knew it was time to give in. He was very peaceful and a few minutes later he died. It was the day after my birthday.

When we celebrated Steven's fortieth birthday, I gave him a ring with an inscription on the inside, closest to him. Faith for the faith that we had in each other; Hope for the hopes we had for family life together; and the Love for the love that we shared. Our faith kept us going through our darkest time. Sadly, many of our hopes will never be fulfilled. But the love will always be there.

Wedding bells

Amanda and Simon had a very different way of looking at things compared with Steven and Ashley. They were very practical. Amanda's breast cancer had come back and they knew the likely outcome. Amanda was the organizer in the family, so she had everything planned for Simon and showed him the finances, the mortgage, everything he would need to know, but at the same time, she was still very positive and was planning things for their two families to do when she got better. She was Steven's colleague at work and it was the two of them who supported each other, chatting on-line when Steven was ill. Steven's wife, Ashley, did not know them well, but they came to her daughter Libby's christening and she went to Amanda's funeral when she passed away a few months after Steven. It was six months later that Ashley met Simon again.

we ♥ our

FAMILY

Eleanor, Naomi, Libby & Yasmin

would love you to come and celebrate the marriage of our

MAM & DAD

I HAD TWO LITTLE GIRLS who had lost their dad and Simon had two little girls who had lost their mam. I used to send him the occasional text just to keep in touch saying, "How are things going, how's the kids?" and one day he replied that his kids were struggling and having a bit of a bad time, so I suggested that perhaps our kids should get together. We took them out for tea and they played happily together. Then when we moved into our new house I invited him and some other friends to come with their children to play in the garden. However, when I had a house-warming party and a mutual friend asked if I had considered going out with Simon, I was shocked; just because two people had lost their partners was no reason for them to get together as a couple. Simon had his own good friends and he certainly didn't need me.

As time passed, we discovered we had lots of other things in common as well as cancer and the kids, and that was fun. One day, when chatting with friends, we both mentioned a film we thought we'd like to see and we wondered if we would go to see it together, but we weren't sure if we should. In the end we did and, of course, my mam wanted to know what was happening and I had to make it very clear we were just friends. I enjoyed his company and I liked him, but did I like him because he was a dad with two little girls in the same position as me? It was still very soon for both of us after our loss and we could easily get things mixed up; we were good friends and the children got on together, but it could become very complicated if we weren't careful, so we didn't arrange anything else. It was just 'Thanks for a nice night out'.

After another three months we did decide to go to the cinema again, but the programme times didn't suit and we went for a drink instead. As we talked, we began to realise that our feelings were rather more than we thought originally and we started to meet more often, but always in secret. It was lovely, but we didn't know what our real feelings were. Was it loneliness? Was it the children? We didn't want to upset them or our families and we kept it secret for a long time. Eventually, of course, when we told some of our friends they all said, "We knew!"

But for us, there was a lot of guilt in those first few months. We felt guilty because he wasn't Steven and I wasn't Amanda, and we felt that we shouldn't have been in a situation where we were with somebody else. Also, Simon feels guilty because he feels it should have been him who had the cancer, not his wife, Amanda. He should have died and she should be here now for their kids. I feel guilty because, to start with, it was Steven who wanted a family more than me. He was desperate for kids, but I put it off because I wasn't ready. I changed my mind about a year after we were married, but sometimes I think he was more maternal than me. It helps to know that he gave me his blessing and to know that he loved Simon.

It's more than five years since Steven died and Simon and I have been together for three and a half years. We kept the children out of it until we were sure and it was only then that we all moved in all together. I was very wary to start with, but they adapted straight away. Before we told them anything, while we were still keeping it quiet, Eleanor, who was still seven, had asked me if Simon was my new boyfriend and when I said no, she said, "Oh, I just thought he might be." Libby was very young, so in many ways it was just El and me and she had me nearly all to herself, so I decided to involve her a little bit. I asked her if she liked Simon and she said she did. "So would you like him to be my boyfriend?"

"Oh, has he asked you?"

"Well, yes he has."

At this, she became very excited and wanted to know more. I explained that we had talked about it and I had said I would think about it but wanted to speak with her about it first.

"Well, tell him yes," was her immediate reply. "And ring him now."

I said I would call him later, but she insisted. "Ring him now," so I did.

"I've got Eleanor here and she says yes, you can be my boyfriend."

He was delighted and said, "Tell her thank you very much and I'm so pleased."

And with that, I had Steven's blessing and Eleanor's too.

Eleanor is very much a Daddy's Girl and although she idolises Simon, she was wary of our affection together at first and how it might affect her. Now that we have talked about it together, and she knows we all love each other just as much as before, she's fine. So are Steven's mam and Amanda's mam; they both love the bairns and have all four of them round. Simon and I both had houses and when we moved in together we thought about extending one of them to make more room, but we realised we needed 'our' house for us as we are now, so we sold up and bought a new one for all of us.

When we started to get to know each other and found ourselves becoming closer, there was sometimes an awful feeling that we might not love each other as much as we loved Steven and Amanda. Also, we both had bad days with grief, but were frightened to admit to our feelings in case we upset each other. Now, as our self-confidence and our confidence in each other has grown, we have learned to be open and say when we are feeling low and so can help each other. We understand that it probably won't be the same as before, because we had so many special things together and we had our children together and that was, and still is, a massive bond. However, we have discovered that, although it is different, it's equally good and we will be married very soon.

Last summer, we went on holiday with our four girls and some friends. One afternoon, returning to our villa, Simon and the girls disappeared into the bedroom and I heard lots of whispering. Then they all came out; Libby knelt down and held out a small box for me. It was an engagement ring. Simon asked, "Will you?" and I said, "Yes!" – and the children have sent out the invitations to our wedding.

Doctors don't do raw emotion

As Professor of Oncology and Chief Medical Officer of a national cancer charity, Jane has many years' experience treating and supporting patients with cancer and their families. When her husband died, did her medical experience help with her own profound and sudden loss?

ARRIVING HOME one Friday evening, I found my husband dead on the stairs. His death was entirely unexpected. Two days earlier, our only daughter, aged eighteen, had gone up to Oxford to start university.

On hearing the news, my sisters came and we all went to be with my daughter so she could at least try to engage with new university life. Oxford, with its buildings and atmosphere, is a good place to mourn and her college held a special choral evensong for us. The funeral was very important, too, with people from every phase of Peter's life. We laughed when we reached the house after the cremation because it was packed with so many people we couldn't get in! We were surrounded by many wonderful friends and family members and we gave Peter an absolutely fabulous send off.

Modern technology was also a great help. Receiving letters afterwards was important, but immediately after Peter died, everybody texted me, which was wonderful. It's so quick, you know that people know, they have heard, you don't have the pain of telling them, and people know that they have said something to you. I had not reckoned on a mobile phone being so useful in this way.

Our daughter was very shaken up when her dad died. After the funeral, she said, "My dad had a life didn't he?" – which was the whole point of the funeral. It was important for her to hear about him from his friends and colleagues, for her to know he 'had a life', and this certainly helped her a great deal. Nonetheless, she found it very difficult to settle at university. She did not make the connection between how she was feeling, her sense of inadequacy, her inability to make decisions and her inability to connect with grief.

As for me, I was fine that first year. I was so focused on my daughter I was completely distracted from grieving, like a little hamster on a wheel. She was finding it tough, but the following summer there was a moment when she was with friends and she suddenly realised she was having fun. As she said later, "A veil lifted from my eyes and I took my life off hold, and started it again." After that, I could see that she had decided she could do it, she was formulating a plan, she would take a year out from university and then go back and start again. She got through her first year at Oxford, passed her exams and did just that.

A lot of people say the second year is the worst and, for me, that was true; I experienced exactly the same thing as my daughter. I lost my *joie de vivre*, I couldn't make decisions and I couldn't make the connection between that and a failure to process my husband's death. It took a counselling person to unpick that for me. I didn't 'do counselling' and would never have gone to a counsellor, but a work colleague could see I was struggling and suggested that I go to an 'executive coach'. The coach explained, from a professional perspective, that you have to maintain your professional identity even when things are happening all around you, and you have to learn how to maintain the ability to make decisions and keep going. You think you're going senile, that it's just the start of the decline, and you don't register that it's connected to grief. My daughter, struggling during her first year at university, hadn't realised that and now I wasn't recognising it, either. She came out of it through talking with her friends; I came out of it through the counselling process – but it was rock music that got me started.

Peter and I had always done a lot of classical music together, so music was very much part of our set-up. Opera and classical music were our background, but when Peter died, I couldn't bear to listen to it. If I listened to any classical music, I just cried. Radio 3 was off limits, no concerts, no opera and I found the only thing I could listen to was sixties rock. It was vaguely familiar from my youth and I had been to a Beatles concert, but I never did rock.

I found a CD in an Oxfam shop and bought it on impulse. It was Keith Richards' first solo album, *Talk Is Cheap*. I had it with me in the car when staying at our house in France. I drove through the back roads of France blasting out Keith Richards, and found I got a real buzz from it. To my surprise, it was enormously helpful, because it showed me there was some fun out there if you go out and look for it. Then, my daughter got me a ticket for the Stones' concert in Hyde Park and it was fantastic. During the first months after bereavement, you do feel that things are never going to get better; you can adjust, but it won't get better. But, just like my daughter, recognising a feeling that life could be fun again gave me hope: hope that things could get better. Watching those septuagenarians leaping around on the Hyde Park stage and having a ball – sod it! Life is not all downhill from here!

I admit I was astonished that I took to Keith Richards, as were all my friends: what was this strange obsession with an ageing rock musician! Brian Eno wrote about the value of music that is emotionally neutral, but that was not what I needed. I needed music that was emotionally charged, but did not make me cry, and I found that the Stones' best music gets to your gut; it's music below the neck. I'm back into classical music now, but it took nearly a year before I was comfortable listening to it again. Gradually, I realised it is possible to re-frame, to re-invent yourself.

The first thing to do was to change the hall in our home, because I couldn't open the door without seeing Peter there. The image of seeing someone dead stays with you for a very long time and it's hard to banish that vision, but there are ways to protect yourself. The carpet had to go and I completely re-decorated the hall within a month.

Most recently, I have re-modelled the house. I haven't touched my daughter's room and everything we have done in the house we have done together because she needs to feel it is still her home as well as mine. Also, after Peter died, I found it very difficult to sleep in the house on my own. Indeed, for the first month or so, each evening at about eleven o'clock, I went round to a friend's house and slept there. Since returning to sleeping at home, I have moved to a different bedroom, so what was our room is now the spare room.

I have been fortunate, because in our family, we talk about things all the time;

we don't bottle things up. I also knew lots of people who had dealt with bereavement and weren't worried about talking about it and that was a great help, too. They understood how I might feel, that I might cry halfway through supper, and that was all right. In the couple of weeks between Peter's death and the funeral, we emptied his wine cellar. Friends would come round and cook a meal and mystery bottles appeared so we had cod and chips with Chateau Whatever.

However, something probably common to most doctors is they think their patients are vulnerable when faced with bereavement and yet they themselves are able to cope. We've had the funeral, we've had the emotion, we now move on. You just keep the lid on it. That's what happened when I went to see the executive coach, allegedly to talk about work. She said, "You haven't dealt with this, have you?" and I spent the whole of the first session in tears. Then the next time, and on several other occasions, I found it difficult to actually go into the counselling room because it was so painful. Most doctors don't do bringing out raw emotion, we don't allow ourselves to feel these emotions, and we rationalise it. For me, my previous experience as a doctor and an oncologist didn't help at all.

Has bereavement changed me? Yes. All my assumptions for life have changed. We were planning on early retirement and those plans went completely up the spout. I have always had a group of friends of my own with whom I did things, but I was now on my own and had to develop a new set of friends because everyone you know is a couple. Although being a widow in your sixties is probably easier than being a divorcee – as a friend said, "Being a widow is an honourable estate" – it does raise completely new issues that you've never thought about for a very long time. Finding new friends, and reconnecting with some who I had known in the past, has given me a framework for my new life.

Some of the practical things, the paperwork that had to be sorted, the bank account and shop accounts, were incredibly oppressive and upsetting. You have to take a registered copy of the death certificate to close some accounts and if their customer services make a mistake, they expect you to do it all again. They do not seem to realise that each time you hand over the death certificate, it is a reminder and each time you want to cry. And the first funeral you go to is a shocker, too.

The good thing is that my bereavement experience has made me think laterally. I have talked with friends who have been bereaved and interviewed several rock stars as part of my "rock star project" and appreciated how people think differently about cancer. I've discovered that even famous people, who have access to every resource in the book, do not necessarily get the information they need about their cancer, or the possible effect of treatment on their work or lifestyle. My experience has widened my horizons in unexpected ways. It's more than four years since Peter died and there are still some things I haven't got quite right, but life is fun again, and I have hope.

A chemotherapy diary

*The common saying 'Everybody is different' certainly applies to cancer chemotherapy;
some have no unwanted side effects and feel fine, while for others it is a struggle.
Here is just one person's story taken from her daily diary over five months.*

Cycle 1

Day 1. I'm due for six cycles of breast cancer chemotherapy, so here goes – my first chemo treatment!

Day 2. Woke with headache, but felt better so went shopping.

Day 3. Nauseated, so took the anti-sickness tablets. Made me sleepy, slept for eleven hours!

Day 4. I'm feeling very tired, but coping better than yesterday. Appetite poor, a 'little of what you fancy' feels better.

Day 5. Prepared cooking for family christening. Once the people arrived, I felt a power of strength coming from nowhere. Tried to have a drink to socialise, but my stomach wasn't having any of it!

Day 7. I've never believed in God. I was quite a sceptic, but to be honest, I did ask him for help as I hadn't a clue what was happening to me today. I have mouth ulcers which are quite sore. Had a terrible time trying to get a chemist to supply the medication; finally found one who would order it and deliver tomorrow. I've just made a chicken dinner and ate all of it. Delicious!

Day 10. My goodness! Woke with no bone pain, no feeling sick, and even had a cup of coffee! Hope this is the road of getting better before my next chemo.

Day 11. Feeling a lot better today, so am going to visit Mum and go out for tea tonight. It was lovely getting out of the house, then watching a film on the telly with a glass of Baileys.

Day 12. Feeling quite sluggish, probably off the Baileys last night! I need to pull myself together. Had a Chinese for supper; these steroids make me have a huge appetite.

Day 13. Woke up at 6am feeling nausea and a headache. Went into office for three hours work, but became too tired. My hair has been shedding all day. It's getting embarrassing, bits of hair flying all over the place. Might have to shave it off earlier than expected.

Day 14. Took Mam out for lunch. I want her to see me at my best as I don't want to worry her.

Day 15. Had a facial today to cheer me up, but couldn't take this hair falling into my food anymore, so called for my daughters to shave it all off. It feels so light now as it was actually hurting my scalp. I feel so much better: I've got my hair piece to wear so nobody will notice.

Day 16. Another good day, woke up and looked in the mirror. Ha Ha! Thank goodness they say beauty is skin deep. I only have one breast and I'm totally bald. Thank goodness for makeup, false eye lashes and pencilled-in eye brows, not forgetting my tan cream. Ha! Eat your heart out chemotherapy! I had a lovely day, made a dinner for everyone and totally enjoyed it.

Day 17. Woke up feeling good, cleaned the car out and polished the windows. Felt shattered, had a cup of coffee and pulled myself around. Visited friends. Shattered again. Early night.

Day 18. Had a poor night's sleep, flu like symptoms, sore throat, head feels on fire and scalp is sore. Getting conscious of my weight, too – put on a few pounds.

Day 20. Had a lovely night's sleep. Going to see oncologist tomorrow, start of my second cycle.

Cycle 2

Pre-treatment blood samples taken today. Started Movicol as treatment can give you constipation. My mind gets so confused at times, even when I write things on paper. Oooops, I hope it's the chemo brain syndrome. Early bed for my big day tomorrow.

Day 1. Quite nervous waiting for the nurses coming to give my chemo. Things worked out well. Tried a different anti-sickness tablet and have more dexamethasone (steroid). I'm going to be in fairy land for a few days.

Day 2. It's 2am and I'm wide awake. 5.30am and still awake. Those steroids have something to answer for. I have gone into auto pilot, thoughts flying through my mind. Biggest thoughts are of my children and grandchildren, how proud I am of all of them. I am carrying a golden bag and in this bag is my dear family. It is a dark forest at times, but in that forest there is a bright light and I feel myself getting closer to the end with my gold bag in my hand.

Day 4. Good night's sleep. Had some scrambled egg on toast and have kept it down so far. Slept all day. Never in my life have I slept so much. Got up at 6.30pm to face the world, but straight back to bed till next morning.

Day 5. Woke up 10am. Haven't a clue where I have been for the past four days.

Day 6. Irritable all day, not sure what to do with myself. Mood swings are awful, cannot settle in one place more than a few minutes.

Day 8. Energy levels coming back, still need afternoon nap, appetite getting better, made homemade soup with garlic and ginger.

Day 10. Out of bed early, feeling a lot better but can't do the things I used to, like cleaning the house.

Day 13. Sun is shining outside. Going out for lunch with the family to mark the first anniversary of my dad dying. Sad occasion, but I'm sure we'll get through it.

Day 17. Starting to wake up through the night. Got a funny feeling depression is just around the corner. I think I need some help like counselling as I am starting to withdraw into myself. Feel I have had no back-up. I have enough stress at the moment, never mind having my money dropped. Just totally do not understand.

154

Day 18. Feeling a little better, but get quite confused. Sometimes have to stop and think before saying things. It's quite scary at times. When I'm writing things spelling is back to front. Thank goodness for spell check on the computer!

Day 19. Made loads of cakes for the village fete. Had a lovely day.

Day 21. Feeling much better. Last day of cycle 2. Let's see what cycle 3 brings.

Cycle 3

Day 1. Went very smoothly. I should feel much better than last time.

Day 7. Woke up to a nice, bright morning. Have put a lot of weight on, not being motivated as usual. Had a curry tonight and couldn't taste a thing.

Day 11. I'm coming to terms that my body cannot do what I want it to do, even though my mind is very active. Went to see Harry Potter with my grandson. Had a lovely day, even though he wanted to hold my hand while crossing the road in case I fell, bless him.

Day 13. Up early to get the Sunday dinner on for the family to arrive. Then we are having a family afternoon out at the park. Thoroughly enjoyed myself. Soon got tired and took myself home earlier than anybody else.

Day 18. My granddaughter is born! Quite a busy day of joy, laughter and tears.

Day 19. Feeling very nauseated after drinking wine last night to celebrate the new arrival. Gone are the days of celebrating!

Day 20. Up early to drop my son off at work for 7.30 then back to bed for an hour.

Day 21. Have quite a bit of fluid where I had my surgery, need it drained off.

Cycle 4

Day 1. Am very apprehensive as I am more aware of what I will be like after chemo. Never mind, the nurse is here who has a great sense of humour.

Day 5. Up early to drop son off at football, then back home to do loads of trips to the charity horse show. Had a very busy day.

Day 6. Got my prosthesis fitted today at the hospital. Had to pay £20 for a bra to support my jelly boob. The 'Appliance Room' was a cupboard that staff use for fittings. Quite degrading really.

Cycle 5

Day 1. Chemotherapy again today. Looking forward to it like a hole in the head!

Day 2. Need the breast area aspirated as I have quite a lot of fluid again.

Day 6. Had a nice, quiet day. No medication or side effects.

Day 15. Getting ready for my first catwalk rehearsal for the cancer charity show. On with the collagen to bounce! Only the odd eyelash left, so the false lashes are going on. Very nervous, but I have to do this for the charity and to boost the confidence of other people going through the same treatment.

Cycle 6

Day 1. Final chemo today! Feeling quite nervous, but don't know why. It's been quite a roller-coaster. Hair starting to grow, fluffy salt and pepper colour.

Day 6. Fashion show rehearsal today! It is so inspiring being with other women who have been through the same experience. When I step out on the catwalk for the last time my last song will be 'I'm Alive!' by Celine Dion. Fab!

Day 22. *I have finished my chemo!!!!!!* I just want to thank my children and grandchildren for helping me get through it.

Three mistakes
that should not be repeated

Mistake number 1
I ignored my symptoms and it was two years before I acknowledged that something must be wrong somewhere down below. Eventually, I accepted that action was needed. First an appointment to see the doc and then the hospital specialist: prostate cancer was diagnosed and it was not confined to the prostate gland. I was beginning to wonder if I had left it too late. Things did not look good and guess what? Because of my own lack of action and complacency, and yes, some bravado, it was all down to me.

Mistake number 2

After I learned my diagnosis, I visited the cancer information corner in the hospital. A sterile place. I realise that some people do find these places helpful, but it was not for me. After some time, floundering helplessly amongst row after row of information sheets, I was presented with a multitude of booklets about how cancer would affect my life, living, eating, intimate moments, family and the rest.

Booklets provide some general information, but I needed to *talk* to somebody, a person. Not a busy consultant with only minutes to spare and other patients waiting to be seen. Not a nurse who could have no idea what it is like to be a man who has just been told he has prostate cancer. I needed to talk face to face with people in similar situations who had experienced firsthand what all this would mean to me and my family. Preferably in a friendly, relaxed, safe and comfortable environment, not at the hospital. To me, as a member of the human race, there is an inherent need to communicate, to express feelings and fears, to discuss and try to look for answers. It does seem natural and I think it should be encouraged, however long it takes.

Thankfully, the specialist nurse realised my frustrations and suggested a visit to a little known charity group that might be able to help. Cue … Cancer Connections. What a revelation! This small local charity had been set up by visionary people who had seen a need to help people like me. And it worked. My family and I visited the centre on many occasions, sometimes together and sometimes alone, asking pertinent questions that were relevant at that time. The volunteer helpers and counsellors at the centre were excellent and always put the individual first. No waiting times, no appointments, just being there to cover all eventualities. How refreshing.

Mistake number 3

How does an organisation such as this manage to exist? Thousands of pounds ploughed into advertising on television? High profile expensive events? Mountains of costly literature which soon become out of date as cancer research improves? No, it is simply through the efforts of a small group of individuals who are prepared to give up their time and create what is a really needed resource for cancer sufferers and their families. An environment that allows visitors to express their fears and someone to listen to them and offer what advice they can, having already been there, done that and got the T-shirt. Donations and offers to help or raise money then come flooding in to sustain and develop the charity. Many of these are a means of saying 'Thank you' for their help at a difficult time. And in my particular case, I am still helping and spreading the good work of the charity. Simplistic? Yes, but it does work and, to my mind, could be rolled out easily throughout the country.

Any takers?

Giving something back

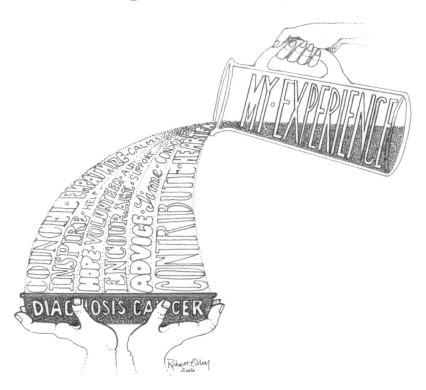

DESPITE THE SIDE EFFECTS of treatment, when you cannot work you need something to fill your mind and your time. In my case, with a background of fourteen years in the Navy, I am now a volunteer with the Sea Cadets. A lot of those kids are deprived, they come from families that have no time for them, and this gives them a chance. I've been lucky with my cancer and this way I can give something back. It's great.

WHEN I DECIDED I would have chemotherapy, I was asked if I would be part of a randomised clinical trial. The drugs would be the same, but they would be given in the standard way every three weeks, or divided up in smaller doses to be given every week. I could not choose one or the other, the treatment was allocated by computer, and the results would not be known for several years, so I would not benefit personally. However, if the trial could help other people, I was happy to contribute. It's good to think that by doing this now, the treatment for others may be better in the future.

BEING A VOLUNTEER working in the charity's office, I know I am useful and helping other people. Sometimes a visitor will ask me about chemotherapy or radiotherapy and if they want to talk about it, I am happy to tell them. We have to be very careful, of course, especially as I had an unusual reaction, but sharing experiences can be helpful.

WHAT MY MUM DIDN'T TELL YOU is that she is now a volunteer, too. She helps with the Drop-In and all sorts of jobs that need doing. After what we went through as a family and all the support we were given, it's lovely that we can both give something back.

WHEN YOU LOSE YOUR HAIR with chemo you can't hide it and when you see people looking it can be upsetting. Now I know what it's like and when I see another woman who's having chemo I think, 'Good for you, you're getting out, there's nothing to be embarrassed about', so I smile and say 'hi'.

I WAS SO GRATEFUL for the help I received when I was diagnosed I felt I needed to help other people in return, especially in view of my own type of cancer and its possible link to sunbathing. The best thing I could do would be to talk to young people and tell them the dangers of sunbeds and sunbathing. I developed a programme, made enquiries with the education authorities and succeeded in obtaining funding to spend five hours each week visiting local schools and colleges. Over the next year, I was able to teach more than 2,500 children and teenagers about the risks of sunbeds, the need for protection when out in the sun and the connection with skin cancer. I have since moved to Canada with my family and that teaching came to an end, but I still hope that some of those young people will have been able to learn from my experience.

AT SCHOOL I sometimes wondered about doing medicine, but it was never a serious idea. I was squeamish and couldn't stand the sight of blood and studied biomedical sciences instead. After the cancer, thinking about the care I had received, especially the difference that the oncologist, Dr Mallik, had made, it inspired me. I wanted to be that person.

I wanted to be that doctor for someone. Even if it was for only one patient, whatever illness they were having, if I could make their experience a little bit better, that is what I wanted to do. So, having graduated in biomedical sciences I did work experience, volunteered in a hospice and a special needs school, applied to Newcastle Medical School, graduated last year – and here I am doing my first hospital job. And I'm a volunteer with Butterflies, helping other young people who have thyroid cancer.

I ALWAYS HAD A GREAT ADMIRATION for the nurses who nursed, cajoled and got me through the possibilities of an early death, but I was well paid in the shipyard, so I was never going to leave that. However, in the end I went back to college and did five O levels and an A level and did my nurse training, always with the intention of working on the ward where I had received my chemotherapy. Following graduation, I was appointed staff nurse on that very same ward and spent seven happy years working there. From there, I moved to another chemotherapy unit, worked in the community and then came to our local hospital as Head of Service for chemotherapy and Senior Nurse Specialist for haematology, caring for patients with the same cancer that I had experienced decades earlier.

THE ELEVEN HOUR OPERATION went well and I was back home after a week, but because they had taken two lots of tissue and muscle from the front of my tummy for the reconstruction I was very cautious about physical activity. Two months later, however, I felt the need to do something and decided to start walking regularly which then developed into power walking. But I needed a goal, a challenge. The Great North Run, wearing a bra, for charity, that was what I would do, 'Because I can'! Two friends joined me, we trained hard, we wore pink bras and power-walked thirteen and a half miles for 'Walk the Walk'. It was hard, but it was fun, it was fabulous, and somebody nominated me for the Spirit of South Tyneside Award which gave me a thousand pounds to give to a charity of my choice. I am delighted with my reconstruction and it's a good feeling being able to help someone else.

LIFE WILL NEVER GET BACK TO 'NORMAL' after cancer, but you learn to cope and I actually feel my life is better now. I have some beautiful people in my life that I would not have without the cancer, and I'm very grateful.

The tree

Precious are the memories we have of you,
we never wanted memories,
we only wanted you.

THE TREE STANDS GUARD by the path to the library; its name is Fagus sylvatica pendula, a Weeping Beech. The library is the hospital library. Standing as it does, close by the path, the tree is passed daily by students, nurses, doctors, all on their way to learn. Small and sturdy, it was planted more than two decades ago by a wife and her daughter in memory of a dearly loved husband and father. At its foot is a small plaque expressing their grief.

The cancer was what would now be termed 'aggressive' and was beginning to grow deep into the bladder wall. There really was no choice; major surgery to remove the bladder was the only option. The operation went well, recovery was good and the future looked promising. But that was not to be. Some of those malignant cells had already escaped and settled elsewhere. Before long they grew, and grew.

It was a few years later that I attended a funeral for someone else and one of the guests said that there were two ladies present at the service who wanted to meet me. Outside, in the garden, they approached smiling in the sunshine. It was a mother and her daughter. "You operated on my husband a number of years ago for bladder cancer. We knew his chances were not good, but you gave our family another eighteen months together with him which were wonderful. When he passed away we planted a tree for him, but we have never had this chance to see you and say 'Thank you'. We want you to know that we have been so grateful for what you did." I was very moved. But grateful? For an operation that did not save their husband and father?

All these years, I have watched that tree grow. Every visit to the library I have stopped, remembered him, and been reminded of my failure. Now I can be more hopeful. I hope the tree will grow for years to come and that at least some young doctor or nurse will see the epitaph, will take a moment to read it, and walk on determined to do better than I did.

Postscript

Cancer Connections, a remarkable story

MANY OF THE CONTRIBUTORS whose stories you have read have, for various reasons, come knocking at the door of Cancer Connections, a ten-year-old cancer support charity in South Tyneside in the North East of England. Some have gained help from other support organisations and some have dealt with the impact of cancer by themselves and the support of family and friends.

When the founders of Cancer Connections first discussed the possible need for a cancer support group they had no idea what might develop. Something small perhaps, local, very informal, run by volunteers who had experienced cancer themselves who would be willing to share their experience with others. Setting up a new charity would be quite an undertaking; was there really a need for a new organisation to provide 'cancer support'? We decided to ask local residents.

Some people said that treatment at the hospital was good and there was a caring hospice, so what else was needed? Others said it would cost too much, and would not be sustainable. Where would volunteers come from? And, in any case, 'People won't come for counselling, you know' and 'Men don't talk about that sort of thing'. However, replies to a questionnaire posted through residents' front doors suggested that a lot of people would appreciate something of this kind. When asked what they would find particularly helpful, eight out of ten requested 'Someone to talk to who understands'. It seemed that our first hunch was right. It was worth a try. Most were very grateful for the treatment they had received from the NHS, but they needed a different kind of help – the sort of personal, emotional and practical help that could only come from someone who had experienced cancer themselves. They were aware that some cancer support groups met on hospital premises, or were associated with hospices, but they would prefer not to return there if it could be avoided. Counselling, massage, complementary therapies, welfare benefits advice, information about cancer treatment would all be helpful but, above all, somewhere local, homely, friendly, comfortable and special where they would feel supported, cared for and safe.

Bearing in mind what we had heard, we visited several other cancer support organisations elsewhere, discussed what we found and then set out a plan. There was no escaping the conclusion that it would have to be quite ambitious, it would require committed volunteers and a certain amount of money. To succeed, it would have to gain the support of the local community, should not duplicate anything already available in the borough, and its activities would be determined solely by local need. And, to provide a homely, non-institutional environment, we would have to buy our own premises. Quite an undertaking, but encouraged by growing support from local people there could be no turning back. What has transpired?

Firstly, we had to set up a registered charity and a company limited by guarantee with trustees who would also act as business directors. The charity had no funds, but grants from The Big Lottery, the Barbour Foundation and several other charitable sources enabled us to make a start. Temporary accommodation was found in a local ecumenical community centre where a small office and a cafe were vacant. We rented the cafe for three afternoons a week, put up posters and printed leaflets. The local paper ran an article about the new charity. Tea, coffee, milk and biscuits were bought. We opened the door and the first visitor came in that afternoon. Within the month, five more followed, then ten in June and twelve in July, all with cancer and all looking for help in some way or another. The number was more than expected.

Tuesday, Wednesday and Thursday afternoons soon became increasingly busy. Requests for counselling soon exceeded the time available from a single volunteer counsellor. Complementary therapies were tried and found to be helpful. Telephone enquiries increased, more and more people gave donations, fundraising events were organised, accounts needed to be kept, administrative tasks began to build up. Extra rooms were rented. The volunteers worked hard, but Cancer Connections was clearly growing far beyond initial expectations.

If we were to respond to the hidden needs of the local community and function as an efficient, credible charitable organisation, professional input was needed for counselling, complementary therapies and administration. Also, larger, more suitable premises would be needed. The original idea was that the charity would buy its own premises. It was time to move, but how? We had no funds.

Late in 2007, a nearby bungalow came onto the market. A visit by some of the volunteers was arranged and the opinion was unanimous: some building work and complete refurbishment would be needed, but it would be ideal. The vendor was approached. He had heard about Cancer Connections and, crucially, he would agree a price and then wait while the money could be found. A fundraising campaign was started; donations started to arrive. Dame Margaret Barbour and her colleagues at the Barbour Foundation contributed £50,000. The Garfield Weston Foundation pledged the same amount if the balance could be found by April 2010. Several other charitable sources contributed, and so did local businesses. With one month to spare, the target sum was reached. Over nine hundred different donors had made it possible, most of them from South Tyneside. Cancer Connections moved into a wonderful new home.

258 Harton Lane is now an extended residential bungalow with reception, lounge, kitchen-diner, children's room and outside play area, conservatory, counselling rooms, complementary therapy room, shower, offices and a peaceful garden. Volunteers have chosen all the furnishings, done all the painting and decorating, and planted the garden. It is a real 'home from home' which, for several years, has won a Macmillan Cancer Environment Award.

We are open 9am to 5pm Monday to Friday and visitors can 'drop in' at any time. There is always someone with experience of cancer available to greet and talk with visitors – 'someone who understands'. Anyone affected by cancer is welcome; the person with cancer, their partner or family, children, carers or people bereaved by cancer. Over the past ten years, more than 4,000 people have sought our help. About half are referred by their GP or specialist nurses; our other visitors seek help for themselves through word of mouth. Latest analysis shows that 46% had cancer and 30% have been bereaved by cancer. 30% of visitors were men and 11% were children or teenagers. People seeking help are sometimes distressed and need help urgently, so we do not keep them waiting. One of our counsellors can see a new visitor within forty-eight hours if needed; there is no waiting list. Complementary therapies do not cure cancer, but can make a big difference. With a team of three therapists they, too, can start immediately; if someone is too ill to leave their home we can visit them.

When Cancer Connections started, we did not appreciate the devastating impact cancer could have on a family's finances. By the time treatment has finished some of our visitors have lost their jobs while others struggle for months, wondering how they will pay the bills and even where the next meal will come from. With a grant from Macmillan Cancer Support, we have an experienced full-time Welfare Benefits Advisor who can help visitors with benefits claims, and to access other sources of funding if needed. To date, visitors have been helped to obtain over £3million of benefits.

All this is provided free of charge but, you may ask, how is that possible in an area of social deprivation? Quite simply, the generosity of the local community and some help from our friends.

It has been suggested that Cancer Connections should be replicated elsewhere given that there are many people with cancer who do not have access to this sort of help, a suggestion with which we would agree. If the stories you have read here inspire you to consider creating your own Cancer Connections we would be delighted, but be warned, the success of any new similar venture will depend entirely on the commitment, determination, enthusiasm, time and effort of a nucleus of volunteers who understand what it is like to have cancer, together with the ongoing backing of your local community. We wish you well.

Index

Acknowledgements

IN ADDITION TO THE CONTRIBUTORS who have been willing to share their personal experiences throughout the pages of this book, I wish to record my thanks to the other people whose help has been invaluable.

For many, cancer is a daunting, humourless topic, but for Robert Olley, the opportunity to respond, as an artist, to the emotions contained in the stories I gave him to read is one that he has relished. Bob, your illustrations have enlightened, enlivened and transformed this book. Thank you.

Having written only medical and scientific texts in the past, it soon became very obvious that I would need help in compiling a book about cancer for the general, non-medical public. Dr Antoinette Geoghegan, psychotherapist and child psychiatrist, and Professor Colin Biott, previously Professor of Professional Education and Development, Northumbria University, have read the many manuscripts and offered apposite and insightful editorial and contextual suggestions, for which I am most grateful. The proofreading skills of Christianne Guillotte and Carol Butler are very much appreciated and Miriam Ahmed, senior counsellor at Cancer Connections, has been a great help through her suggestions, discussions and enthusiasm for the undertaking.

Writing is a time-consuming, solitary occupation that constrains other activities. To Val, my wife, my loving thanks for your encouragement and patience.

Not all stories in this book have had a happy ending: in recent weeks, Audrey has passed away and Lee, too, has learned the answer to his question. Both, in their different ways, were an inspiration while they were with us and I hope will continue to inspire many others who turn these pages.

RRH (June 2017)

**The Queen's Award
for Voluntary Service**

In June 2015, Cancer Connections received a
Queen's Award for Voluntary Service

*****

To learn more about Cancer Connections visit
www.cancerconnections.org.uk

*****

Publication funded by Cllr Richard Porthouse South Tyneside Mayoral Appeal 2015–6
and sponsorship for Ms Wendy Judge in the Ponteland Triathlon 2016.

All the contributors, including Robert Olley and the editor, have done so free of charge.
Profits from the sale of the book will go to Cancer Connections Ltd.

About the Artist

Robert 'Bob' Olley is an artist and sculptor best known for his mining subjects, humorous drawings and paintings of everyday life. Born into a South Shields mining family in 1940, he began his working life in 1955 as a painter and decorator before going into the mining industry in which he spent eleven years at Whitburn Colliery, until the pit closed in 1968. Leaving the industry, he joined Plessey Telecoms but, developing his artistic talents, he became a full-time professional painter and sculptor in 1974. Bob has undertaken many commissions for the BBC, Tyne Tees television, hospitals, theatres and boroughs including artwork, murals and sculpture. His work can be seen throughout the North East, in France and in many private collections.

About the Editor

Prior to retirement, Reg Hall was Consultant Urological Surgeon at the Newcastle upon Tyne Hospitals NHS Trust, Macmillan Lead Clinician and Director of the Northern Cancer Network, and Visiting Professor in the University of Newcastle upon Tyne. Born in 1939, he studied medicine at University College and University College Hospital, London. Following postgraduate training in London and Newcastle, together with research at the Royal College of Surgeons of England and the Institute for Cancer Research, he was appointed consultant in 1974. In addition to his work in the NHS, for more than thirty years he has worked with colleagues at the Medical Research Council and the European Organisation for Research in the Treatment of Cancer in the development and conduct of national and international cancer clinical trials. Following retirement in 2004, he initiated and co-founded Cancer Connections, a cancer support charity in the northeast of England where he still helps as a volunteer.